Local Food Ecosystems

How Food Hubs Can Help Create a More Sustainable Food System

Local Food Ecosystems

How Food Hubs Can Help Create a
More Sustainable Food System

Duncan Catchpole

JANUS PUBLISHING COMPANY LTD
Cambridge, England

First published in Great Britain 2021
by Janus Publishing Company Ltd
The Studio
High Green
Great Shelford
Cambridge CB22 5EG

www.januspublishing.co.uk

British Library Cataloguing-in-Publication Data
A catalogue record for this book is available from the British Library

ISBN 978-1-85756-918-6

Cover Design: Shuk-Yee Lee

Printed and bound in Great Britain

MIX
Paper from
responsible sources
FSC® C014540
FSC
www.fsc.org

Contents

Foreword

Because of the manner in which many people in Western societies tend to think, it is easy to believe that our world is comprised of a series of linear binary connections, where outcomes are shaped through simple causes and effects, with our decisions and actions leading to more or less predictable results. This is, however, very far from how things actually work. The human world, and indeed the natural world that sustains it, works as a system, and through webs of connections whereby change in one part can cause sometimes unpredictable ramifications far away in time and space.

As our world begins to wake up to the grave emergencies of climate change, ecosystem degradation and mass extinction, it is vital that we shift our thinking, so as to recognise the limitations of what are apparently simple single solutions, and instead take a system-wide view. It is especially vital that we urgently apply such thinking to our food system, because attention to how we feed ourselves must be central to resolving many of the challenges that lie before us.

For while it might seem that it is plastic waste drifting in the sea, planes polluting the skies and car exhausts choking our cities that pose the biggest threats to the ecological well-being of the world, we are discovering that it is in fact our food system that is the gravest cause of damage to the web of life upon which we all depend.

The different issues embedded in our food system are now well documented. Take the continuing deforestation that is driven by large-scale agricultural expansion, such as for cattle and soya production in the Amazon and oil palm plantations in Asia. After land is cleared and under intensive production, there is the progressive loss of soil and the application of fertilisers and pesticides, all of which cause profound impacts on land, air and water. These changes lead to species loss, degradation of ecosystem services and carbon emissions.

And while such an approach has been driven by the assumption that the world is short of food, and that food must be as cheap as possible, neither is true. Today the human population suffers more from obesity than hunger, while the consequences of how we produce are seen in a wide range of societal costs that are not reflected in supermarket prices. Bare hillsides cleared to produce sheep increase flood risk and raise insurance premiums. Cheap, unhealthy calories cause a range of impacts that load massive costs to public health services. Carbon emissions from soils and forests contribute to sea level rise and extreme weather, both of which are already causing massive economic costs. Once you start to look, then our food is far from cheap.

Indeed, elements of our food system are linked with the biggest economic crisis in history. The Covid 19 pandemic appears to have originated in a market where wild animals were being traded for food, and this is not the only linkage between how we feed ourselves and risks of pandemic disease. For example, deforestation is a source of disease risk in humans, as seen in the Ebola outbreaks in Africa. Other viral outbreaks that risked massive loss of life came from factory-farmed chickens and pigs.

The way we have chosen to feed ourselves has relied less and less on ecology and more and more on industrial models, based on ever more sophisticated technology. For some decades, it appeared to be a successful model, enabling output to keep pace with explosive human population growth. Now, however, the limitations inherent in an approach that trades massive output of inexpensive food against the environment and public health are becoming ever starker. Indeed, the major threats to food security in the future are increasingly environmental in nature, with yields already being hit in different parts of the world by soil damage, extreme weather and water scarcity.

So much for where we are – the big question now is where we are going.

Many new models and ideas have become evident during recent years. Organic and other low-input production methods that cut emissions, save resources and restore soils; lower meat and dairy consumption that relieves pressure on land and resources; new policies that will switch subsidies into payments for environmental improvements; culture change to reduce food waste; shorter supply chains that connect people with food near to where they live; landscape level planning to weave mosaics of wildlife-rich habitat into farmed land. All of this is positive, and of course every element of the switch to a sustainable food system is linked to each of the others, thereby underlining the need for a system, and indeed ecosystem, approach.

This is why I have been so encouraged to learn more about the Cambridge Food Hub, and the initiative they're taking to foster a local food ecosystem that meets head on all of the challenges that we must grapple with, and in a positive way, through finding a sustainable niche for all of the mutually interdependent components that must work in harmony for the whole to function.

As a resident of Cambridge, I look forward to seeing the Hub making the impact it sets out to achieve, and I very much hope it will be an inspiration for other comparable initiatives.

Tony Juniper CBE, environmentalist and writer.

Preface

The notion of the 'climate emergency' is burgeoning within society's collective conscience, and this notion is married to an understanding that 'we are responsible'. It is widely accepted that 'system change' is desperately needed, although it is less clear exactly what system change looks like, and who is going to make it happen.

The finger of blame for climate change points in the direction of industry and commerce. Industry has developed an insatiable appetite for the world's natural resources, and the reason for this is because the economic model which underpins it has 'Capital and Growth' as its bedrock. Money reigns supreme. 'Capital and Growth' are the ultimate principles governing our lives.

These principles are far from flawless.

Money is a human invention, and like everything manmade, it isn't perfect. It distorts the true value of things. Consider the respective value of a Rolex watch and a glass of water. One costs £3,500 in a high street jeweller, the other is available for free in the café next door. Imagine if you approached the owner of the watch and asked them if they would exchange it for a glass of water. They would almost certainly say 'no'. Now imagine the same scenario, but this time in the desert, a day's walk from the nearest settlement. Now the watch is a fairly useless trinket, whereas the water will sustain life long enough to reach safety. The watch owner would gladly exchange ten watches for the glass of water.

This analogy demonstrates how money distorts the true value of things. In a world governed by the principles of 'Capital and Growth', the items that are revered the most are often the ones which play the most arbitrary, superficial roles in our lives, while the things that really matter are completely taken for granted. Only in a world governed by Capital and Growth would it be credible to decimate an acre of wilderness in order to mine a kilogram of gold. Only in a world governed by Capital and Growth would the tusks of an elephant be considered more valuable anywhere other than attached to the elephant that grew them.

The analogy demonstrates the fundamental flaw of the Capital and Growth economy. In the analogy the watch represents the global GDP, everything in the whole world you can put a price tag on, and the glass of water represents all of the world's natural systems; virtually worthless in monetary terms, but essential for life. When scrutinised under the harsh conditions of the desert the true value of these things is revealed. The desert represents ... yep, you guessed it ... *climate change*. The challenges presented to us by climate change, like the challenging conditions of the hypothetical desert, are forcing us to reassess the true value of things.

The principles of Capital and Growth are flawed because they do not accurately reflect the true value of things. Doesn't it seem absurd, therefore, that 'Capital and Growth' would be the bedrock of the global economy, the ultimate principles that govern our lives?

So, what *should* be the ultimate principles that govern our lives?

There is a set of principles which *are* flawless. They have been around for billions, not hundreds, of years. They are absolute and undeniable. They apply to all life on earth, and indeed the known universe. These are principles of Harmony: the laws of nature.

What if the economy were to have these flawless laws of nature as its bedrock instead of the flawed principles of Capital and Growth? What if business systems were designed to work in Harmony with nature rather than against it? What if we were to replace 'Capital and Growth' with 'Nature and Harmony'?

Redesigning the entire economy is unrealistic. But something which *can* be done, right now, is to start rethinking the role that business plays in society. We can start by creating businesses which have Nature and Harmony as their underlying principles.

Every business should have, as its primary objective, a 'noble purpose': the thing that it does which enriches people's lives and benefits society without exploiting others. But business does not behave this way. Because of the principles of Capital and Growth, the noble purpose is nearly always superseded by another objective: profit.

Having money as its primary motivation actually *undermines* the ability of business to fulfil its true purpose. As an example, consider the food industry. The primary objective of the food industry shouldn't be anything other than *feeding people,* with healthy and sustainably produced food. But this isn't the case. The primary objective of the food industry is to make money. As a result, many people in the world are hungry, food production is unsustainable, and a lot of food is unhealthy. The noble purpose of the food industry has been seriously compromised due to the principles of Capital and Growth. This must change.

Some great work is already being done in designing new economic models which enable us to live within planetary boundaries and which achieve human prosperity. This book is about how this new type of economic thinking can be put into practice in the food industry, and in particular it is about a system that can help us build resilient, healthy and sustainable local food economies.

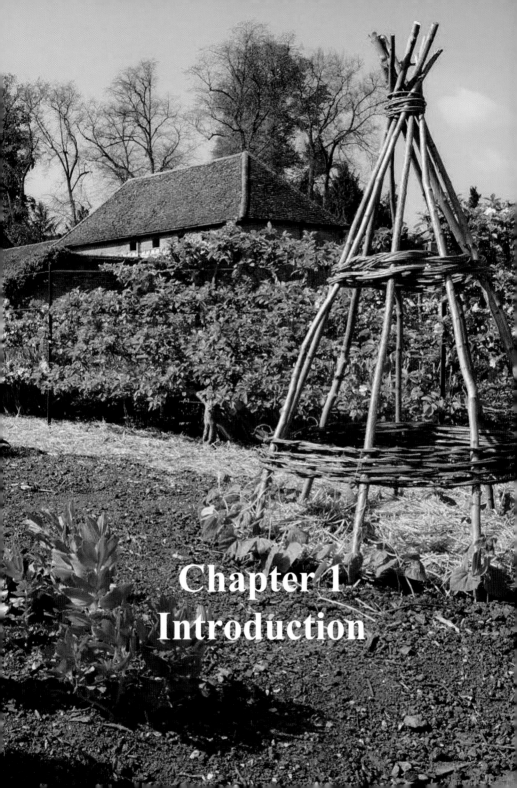

Chapter 1
Introduction

Chapter 1
Introduction

Over the past five or six years my colleagues and I have been developing a new business model for a project taking place in Cambridge, called the Cambridge Food Hub. The business model we have developed is based upon a new concept in the way that food supply chains are structured and managed, that we have called the 'Local Food Ecosystem'. The Local Food Ecosystem is an entire food system, comprising producers, processors, retailers and many other food practitioners. The Food Hub provides services and facilities which enable the members of the Local Food Ecosystem to trade more easily and efficiently with one another.

As the Food Hub project is close to becoming a reality, I felt it was time to write something that would help people understand the concept of the Local Food Ecosystem and to share what I hope will turn out to be a good idea. As you read this book please bear in mind that I am neither an author nor a scholar: I am just a small businessman who simply wants to do things a bit better. The ideas that have come together in the writing of this book are mainly just from my own experience of running an organic food business and from talking to many interesting people over the years who either work with food locally or who campaign for food and environmental sustainability. The opinions expressed are my own, but they come from the heart and I do passionately believe in the potential of the Local Food Ecosystem concept.

Since we began the Food Hub project, and indeed since I began writing this book, the world has undergone a monumental transformation. In March 2020, the UK went into lockdown to help reduce the spread of coronavirus. During the lockdown, food supply chains became a matter of critical national concern, and I am pleased to say that the independent, local food industry rose to the challenge and really shone. Food Hubs and box schemes up and down the country quickly adapted to the change in people's food-sourcing habits, demonstrating the resilience of local food systems. As we look to rebuild in the aftermath of coronavirus, projects such as the Food Hub seem more relevant than ever: the Local Food Ecosystem creates opportunities for people to start their own small food businesses, something that many people who were made redundant as a result of coronavirus have already started to do. It improves the resilience of the food system, ameliorating our chances of coping with the next pandemic, or indeed other factors which may disrupt the supply chain, such as we experienced when we left the single market. But most importantly, it shows a way in which we can 'build back better' and create a food system which is kinder to the planet. Without doubt, the *right time* for the Local Food Ecosystem is *right now*.

I've no way of knowing whether the Food Hub will have the transformative effect we hope it will, but one thing I do know for certain is that we have got to give it a try.

A 'new way'

Seeing as you are reading a book with the subheading 'How Food Hubs Can Help Create a More Sustainable Food System', I'm starting with an assumption that you already take an interest in environmental issues and food sustainability, and that you understand that intensive agriculture and global food systems are causing widespread damage to natural ecosystems and are contributing massively to climate change. I imagine that from time to time you feel a sense of despair when you dwell on the way the world's industry (and not just food, but nearly all industry and commerce) seems to be relentlessly pressing on, obsessed with growth and apparently unconcerned about ecological boundaries. Perhaps you despair because it feels as though decisions affecting the fate of the world are being made in corporate boardrooms in far-away places which you have little or no control over, or worse, you understand that the people in those boardrooms are themselves bound to a certain 'way' of doing things which is very difficult to change.

You are not alone. The call to action I often hear from environmental activists is 'System Change not Climate Change'. This is quite a significant demand. More energy-efficient cars and better recycling aren't going to cut the mustard; these campaigners want a fundamental shift in the 'way' things are done.

Looking beyond the established norm and imagining an entirely different way of doing things is not at all easy, but fortunately there are respected and erudite people who are doing just that. New ideas about economic models which might supersede the incumbent one are emerging, and better still, gaining traction. We are becoming increasingly familiar with the concept of the 'Circular Economy'. Some other examples of ideas about this 'new way' include 'Doughnut Economics' (Kate Raworth), the 'Ecological Integrated Paradigm' (prof. Tim Lang), the 'Living System Model' (Jay Bragdon) and 'An Economy of Love' (David Cadman). Although all of these models and ideas have their own terminology and differ in their detail, they all come from a similar school of thought and share some fundamental characteristics: they all place a higher degree of primacy on living assets such as nature and human prosperity than they do on non-living capital assets. They all promote holistic, circular processes rather than reductionist, linear processes. They all demand existence within ecological boundaries. They all reflect an ideology which is in line

HRH The Prince of Wales addresses the audience at the Harmony in Food and Farming Conference.

with that of the Harmony Project,[1] and the book *Harmony: A New Way of Looking at Our World.*

Right at the outset of this book, the impression of the Local Food Ecosystem that I want to convey is that it is a concept founded on a fundamentally different set of economic principles than those of Capital and Growth. It is, instead, a business system which conforms to these new economic ideas: the new way of doing things that is in accordance with principles of Harmony. In fact, I would say that if you are engaged in the implementation of Circular or Doughnut economics in your area, as there is a very encouraging trend towards at the moment, then establishing a Local Food Ecosystem in your area would go a long way towards achieving your objectives.

Features of a Local Food Ecosystem

The Local Food Ecosystem concept is described in greater detail in Chapters 3 and 4, but I think it's a good idea to summarise the Local Food Ecosystem and give an overall impression of what is meant by it from the outset.

The Local Food Ecosystem is not a business. The term refers to a business *system*; the entire supply chain from farm to consumer. It is an alternative way of structuring the supply chain and coordinating the resources within it. The 'business model' is the Food Hub, which provides services and facilities that enable the functioning of the Local Food Ecosystem.

There are five key points I'd like to make about the Local Food Ecosystem, which hopefully provide a little more clarity about the nature and the purpose of the concept:

- It is a whole new way of doing business, based on principles of Harmony.

- The primary motivation of this system is *feeding people with healthy and sustainably produced food.* Not profit.

---

1. The work of the Harmony Project takes its inspiration from HRH The Prince of Wales' vision, set out in his book *Harmony: A New Way of Looking at Our World*. This vision shows us that when we learn from principles that ensure the resilience and balance of systems in Nature and when we apply this learning to our own lives, we begin to embrace better, healthier ways of living.

- Within the Local Food Ecosystem *everything* finds a destination where it is valued, and nothing goes to waste.
- Food is distributed more equitably throughout the community.
- The system minimises the environmental impact of food.

One thing I want to be clear about is that it is a *business* system we are talking about here. It is not a charity; it doesn't require volunteers or external funding to operate. Later in this book you will read about the 'hybrid business model', a melding together of pure social enterprise and conventional 'for-profit' businesses which together create a values-driven company that generates its own revenue and is financially self-sustaining, successful even. Because of this the Local Food Ecosystem has the potential for big impact.

One other point that I would like to make concerns the degree to which this concept is an 'ideal' food system, and is perhaps best illustrated by this anecdote. A good friend of mine, Brian, kept challenging me whenever I asserted that the Food Hub is a 'sustainable' food system. This irritated me no end; after all, the whole point of the exercise was to improve the sustainability of food. I finally got his point when he asked me to imagine that I was the Food Tsar of the whole world, with the power to redesign the food system from the ground up according to a utopian vision. Of course, given a blank canvas and the opportunity to really 'think big' I would come up with something that was very different to the Food Hub. Thanks to Brian the word 'more' was inserted into the book's subtitle. Had it been left as 'How Food Hubs Can Help Create a Sustainable Food System', this would imply that it was an absolute solution, that I had somehow figured out how to magically transform the global food industry into something which feeds everybody in the world with minimal impact on the environment. As it happens, I do believe that the Local Food Ecosystem is close to being an ideal food system, but only within its own microcosm. Sadly, there is no 'reset' button for the food industry; we have to work within the system that already exists. The Local Food Ecosystem is, at least, an idea for a better way to organise food supply chains that addresses the many food-related problems we face. Significantly though, it *is* something which can sit alongside existing frameworks, and which can be implemented *anywhere* within a short space of time and even with little money if there is the will to do it.

What are the problems?

Normally you might expect a book that was introducing a new business idea to begin by detailing a particular problem which the new idea was designed to address. The book would then go on to describe the solution to that problem, no doubt also mentioning how the solution can be monetised and provide a healthy return on investment. This approach to problem solving often follows the 'reductionist', 'linear' ideology characterised by Capital and Growth, which we are trying to move away from. It addresses the symptoms rather than the cause, and often results in an escalation of problems. To give a crude example: problem: 'My cabbages are infested with aphids'; solution: 'We've invented a powerful insecticide.' Problem: 'The microfauna in the soil has been killed and it is no longer fertile'; solution: 'We've invented a chemical fertiliser.' Problem: 'The chemicals used to make the fertiliser are running out', and so on.

The food system faces a multitude of problems and challenges (a finite supply of chemical elements such as phosphorous for fertiliser manufacture being just one of them). The list of food-related problems includes issues like food waste, food poverty, diet-related ill health, deforestation, soil erosion, water scarcity, waste from packaging, loss of biodiversity, emissions from intensive agriculture, emissions in the supply chain. It is a long list. The thing you have to be mindful of is that these problems are all connected. They are all symptoms of a food system which is not functioning as it should. Dealing with these problems independently is inefficient and ineffective, because you are only addressing the symptoms, not the cause of them. Rather than trying to solve individual problems, the Local Food Ecosystem is a completely different system. A system in which these problems do not exist. And it achieves this because, unlike the current food industry, it considers the food system *as a whole.*

The point I am trying to make is that the Local Food Ecosystem shouldn't be thought of in terms of it being a 'solution' to a particular problem. Later in this book you will read about an instance when 100,000 lettuces went to waste. The Local Food Ecosystem will not prevent that from happening. Nor will it magically find a home for the unwanted lettuces. It is not a solution to that problem. Instead, the Local Food Ecosystem is a microcosm of a much more ideal food system, and

During the coronavirus lockdown many community fridges and community Food Hubs were established, providing donated surplus food for free to people at risk of food insecurity. This all happened thanks to an army of volunteers who so generously gave their time and effort.

within this microcosm no food is being wasted. So while the Local Food Ecosystem does not resolve systemic industrial wastage of food, it does showcase an alternative way of doing things that is much less wasteful. If the microcosm grows, if Local Food Ecosystems start establishing across the country, then we could achieve a situation where a significant proportion of the country's food passes through a waste-free supply chain.

Clearly food waste is one of the food-related issues that the Local Food Ecosystem addresses, but it is not the only one.

One problem which ought to be a particular source of shame for the food industry is food poverty. Because linear food supply chains are commercially driven, the issue of food poverty falls outside the system; there is no opportunity to make money from people who haven't got any. Food poverty is an externalised cost; the burden of addressing it has been passed on to the social security and charitable sectors. If this problem is to be addressed systemically, if we want *all* people to be able to access good-quality, healthy food, then the 'low-income' section of society has to be brought back into the system and considered as part of the whole.

The issue the Food Hub and the Local Food Ecosystem were conceived to address, first and foremost, is the environmental impact of food. I don't know about you, but the prospect of climate change *terrifies* me, and many other people too. It is an issue of incredible magnitude, and it confounds me that governments and powerful corporations are not treating it with the appropriate degree of urgency and severity. There is a multitude of ways in which the food system impacts our environment. Many of these are associated with the way food is produced; however, there is also a significant amount of environmental impact associated with the food supply chain. Food transportation and refrigeration require energy, and therefore emissions. It is these emissions that the Food Hub is particularly targeting.

The key to having a more sustainable, resilient and vibrant food system lies with small food businesses: market gardeners who sell their produce locally, artisanal food manufacturers who process food with love, independent shops that sell local foods.

Whereas environmental sustainability is the greatest motivating issue behind the Food Hub project, the issue that it addresses most directly is the hardship faced by small independent food businesses and the barriers to new food businesses starting up. The key to having a more sustainable, resilient and vibrant food system lies with small food businesses: market gardeners who sell their produce locally, artisanal food manufacturers who process food with love, independent shops that sell local foods. The very best food that money can buy nearly always comes through the independent food business sector. However, the small, independent food business sector is stifled by the global food industry. Its dominance is just so overwhelming. Independent business cannot hope to compete on price. Instead, independent food businesses are forced into the margins, existing either because of specialisation, or by positioning themselves at the exclusive end of the market. Essentially this equates to the gentrification of foods from small businesses, creating a class divide regarding access to local and artisanal foods. Food entrepreneurs are not at fault for this; the critical point is that it is exceptionally hard to make a living running an independent food business. Frankly, most of the small food businesses we love so much only exist through virtue of the fact that they are run by people who care passionately about what they do and who are prepared to work for less money than they deserve, and by having a nucleus of customers who are prepared to pay more for food which has higher values. The result of all this is that it discourages many people from starting their own food business. Why would they if all they are going to do is work extremely hard for such little reward? This is an incredible shame. It means that a wealth of passion and talent remains untapped, that many people are denied the opportunity of an occupation that they would love, and that many more people are denied access to the really good food they would produce.

A complicated idea

> 'Long story short – if it's summarised in a meme, it's probably not going to create a perfect food system. This shit is complicated, let's act like it.'
>
> Professor Garrett M Broad

The Local Food Ecosystem is a radical departure from the way the food industry is currently structured. It is a comprehensive system that addresses many issues, including systemic food waste, food and health inequality, the environmental impact of the food system, and barriers to local food trade. It is also rather complicated.

By and large the business community, especially those who invest in it, do not like complicated ideas. They like simplified processes, solutions to problems that can be conveyed in a catchy elevator pitch.

The Local Food Ecosystem concept cannot be explained in five minutes. But therein lies its strength. The reason why it is so difficult to summarise in an elevator pitch is because it deals with complex social and environmental problems with its own appropriate degree of complexity. I was delighted when my colleague Alice spotted the tweet (above) from Professor Garrett Broad. After repeated frustrating attempts to explain a radical, holistic and complex system in a time-limited presentation, it was marvellous to come across a statement which proclaimed that system change is not a simple matter. Solutions to complicated problems are going to be complicated themselves; there is no quick fix or magic bullet. Thanks to Professor Broad I'm now able to say: 'No, I'm not going to give you the "five-minute version", because it won't make sense. The Local Food Ecosystem is indeed a better way of managing the food supply chain, but if you want to understand it you're just going to have to make yourself comfortable and listen for a while.'

And hence the writing of this book.

What is a Food Hub?

I have, reluctantly, included this section mainly because, in a book that is about Food Hubs, it would be remiss not to include a definition of what a Food Hub actually is.

I say reluctantly because it is quite hard to pin down exactly what 'Food Hub' means. If I said the words 'newsagent', 'patisserie' or 'petrol station' you would instantly know what I was talking about, but there is no archetype of a Food Hub that creates such a vivid impression. The word 'hub' seems to be especially in vogue at the moment and recently there has been a proliferation of 'community hubs', 'student hubs' and, of course, 'Food Hubs'. Because the expression is so open to interpretation, and seems apt for a number of different applications, there is tremendous diversity in the types of enterprise that refer to themselves as Food Hubs; everything from an online platform for ordering takeaway food to an enterprise zone consisting of large-scale food-processing and research businesses, all of which appear to be a perfectly credible implementation of the term.

All the same, the subheading for this book is 'How Food Hubs Can Help Create a More Sustainable Food System', so I'm clearly referring to a certain type of Food Hub, and you've probably guessed that an app which allows you to access pizzas, kebabs and Chinese food through one convenient portal isn't what I had in mind.

The arena in which the term Food Hub appears most prominently is within the sustainable food movement.[2] Here too there is a great deal of

---

2. For further reading, refer to the paper 'Food hubs in the UK: where are we and what next?' by Paola Guzman and Christian Reynolds, published by the Food Research Collaboration, an initiative of the Centre for Food Policy.

diversity in the types of enterprise which identify as being a Food Hub, but there are also a number of common themes. If we look at these areas of convergence it is possible to come up with a broad definition of what a Food Hub is, at least from the sustainable food movement's perspective. In the most part, a Food Hub could be described as a space (which can be physical or virtual, permanent or temporary) for the convening of food enterprises or their products. Typically these enterprises will be from a specific geographical area (i.e. local) and have shared values (e.g. environmental sustainability, artisanal production values). Coming together this way brings mutual benefit to the enterprises who are participating, such as access to markets and economies of scale, and also brings social and environmental benefits, such as shorter supply chains and improved transparency. The role of the Food Hub is to support this community of enterprises through the provision of services and facilities.

Why is local important?

Occasionally people will ask me why it is that such an emphasis is put on local food. They will point out that things like intensive animal agriculture and food waste are much bigger issues than 'food miles' in terms of environmental impact. They are absolutely right. They will point out that growing certain foods in countries with climates that are more suited to producing those crops is more efficient than forcing them to grow locally, in a heated greenhouse for example. Again, this is absolutely correct. So why is it that local is so important?

The list of reasons why buying locally produced food is a good thing goes way beyond simply the reduction of food miles. The benefits of a vibrant local food economy amount to something which is greater than the sum of its parts. Perhaps the greatest of these is also the least tangible and hardest to quantify: eating locally grown food is *great for your well-being*. There's just something about being able to go into your local baker to buy a freshly baked loaf, browsing the goods on offer at a farmers' market or visiting a pick-your-own farm that seems to be the epitome of a very high quality of life. Having a sense of connection with your food is an important aspect of well-being; knowing where it came from, who produced it and the methods and values that were employed. This is the

Being able to buy excellent quality fresh food directly from the producer at a farmers' market epitomises good quality of life.

one thing that the multiple retailers, international brands and global fast-food chains have never managed to replicate.

While food miles may not be up there with intensive animal agriculture in terms of environmental impact, that doesn't mean it isn't an issue that needs to be addressed, especially when you consider the extent of the carbon emissions reduction targets that have been set. There is something rather absurd about food being exported out of an area while food of exactly the same type is being brought in from somewhere else, or strawberries going on a 100-mile round trip in order to end up 5 miles from the place they were produced (something you will read about later in this book). Addressing these issues by ensuring that there is infrastructure in place to ensure that at least some of the food which is being grown in the fields that are close to a particular town or city makes its way directly into that local market surely represents an easy win in terms of carbon savings.

Ranking food in terms of its sustainability rating is an absolute minefield. The subject is riddled with complexity, grey areas and nuance which can make it difficult to determine which foods are the best to choose from an environmental perspective. Is it better to buy organic tomatoes from Spain, or non-organic ones from the next village? Is a highly processed 'fake-meat' burger, including GM soya in its ingredients list and wrapped in plastic packaging, better than a beef burger made from pasture-fed cattle and bought from a local butcher? Factor in social issues such as fair trade and health and it becomes truly mind boggling. However, there is one category of food which sits, unquestionably, at the apex of food sustainability. This is organically grown fruit and vegetables, sourced directly from a local farm. Wouldn't it be great if as much of this type of food as possible found its way onto people's plates?

> *There is one category of food which sits, unquestionably, at the apex of food sustainability. This is organically grown fruit and vegetables, sourced directly from a local farm.*

The final point I would like to make on the topic of whether local food systems are important is to ask you to think for a moment about what the alternative is. This would be a world where *all* food for the home comes from a supermarket, and where the only options for dining out are homogenous chain restaurants. It is a world where control over your diet lies in the hands of large corporations who are less interested in your well-being than they are in their bottom line. That is not for me, and it is not for you either.

Before I go on I want to stress that I don't believe that supermarkets and global food giants are necessarily *evil*. I really don't want to offend anybody who works in such an organisation; I've met many genuinely lovely people who work for supermarkets, quite often at food sustainability events, or workshops to address food waste. What I have a problem with is the *way* things are done in the mainstream food industry, which I believe originates from having misplaced priorities. I would also like to remind you of that cornerstone of Circular Economy thinking, which is *'the most sustainable option is the thing you already have'*. Well, the 'thing' we already have in the food industry is a network of buildings up and down the country which are designed to be outlets for food (i.e. supermarkets).

They will have a role to play as part of our sustainable food future, but that is a topic for a different book.

The evolution of the idea

There was no lightbulb moment when the Local Food Ecosystem concept popped, fully formed, into someone's head. It is a concept that has developed over several years, involving many influences, conversations with food business owners, and trials.

A little more about me for context. I have been involved with local produce and organic food since 1998, when I founded a business called The Cambridge Organic Food Company (COFCO). COFCO is an organic box scheme enterprise, delivering locally grown organic fruit and vegetables to people's homes. It is in my capacity as owner of this business that I occasionally get invited to various meetings and events concerning food sustainability.

One such meeting took place in Cambridge in November of 2013; a consultation meeting to see if Cambridge wanted to join the newly formed 'Sustainable Food Cities'[3] network. Sustainable Food Cities were promoting eight 'key issues', which included things like reducing food poverty, reducing waste, promoting sustainable dietary choices, transforming institutional food procurement and building vibrant local food economies. The delegates attending this meeting were asked to come up with ideas for projects that would address these issues locally. Several of the ideas put forward featured things like 'collaborative workspace', 'a collection point for local produce' and 'a place where people and businesses can come together'. Some of the problems identified were that the lack of affordable commercial buildings and kitchen facilities was a barrier to the creation of new small food businesses, and that there was a lack of infrastructure to support local food trade. The aggregation of these ideas suggested that the most helpful thing for Cambridge in its journey towards becoming a Sustainable Food City was a Food Hub.

---

3. Sustainable Food Cities (now Sustainable Food Places) helps people and places share challenges, explore practical solutions and develop best practice on key food issues. It is a partnership programme run by The Soil Association, Food Matters, and Sustain: the Alliance for Better Food and Farming.

Cambridge Sustainable Food is the organisation responsible for Cambridge's inclusion in the Sustainable Food Places network. Here, they are out in force engaging with the public at Cambridge's leading food festival, Eat Cambridge.

So at the earliest inception of the idea, the Food Hub was an amorphous, vague notion of a food centre that would bring together local producers, local food businesses and other well-meaning organisations. The remit was to create a Food Hub. No one really knew what that meant, but Cambridge wanted a Food Hub, so a Food Hub it would get.

The best way to approach these problems is to re-think the whole system, but this time think of it as a 'whole' system.

I volunteered to take the lead on this project and our small team set about trying to figure out how to realise the vision. The guiding objectives for the Cambridge Food Hub project were the Sustainable Food Cities key issues. Would it be possible to bring together all of these virtuous objectives in one project? Well, as it turns out, yes. In fact, the *best* way to meet these objectives is to consider them all at them same time. These problems do not exist in isolation from one another. They are all symptomatic of an imperfect food system. The best way to approach these problems is to re-think the whole system, but this time think of it as a 'whole' system.

The term 'hub' implies being at the heart or centre of something. At some point the question had to be asked: 'what is it the hub of?'. This is when we became aware of the bigger picture. The Food Hub isn't just about creating a fancy food store, the magic of the Food Hub is that it sits at the centre of something much more significant; *a whole community of local food enterprises*. The thing is, one independent shop selling sustainable food is great, but isn't going to make a huge difference. A farm converting to organic is brilliant, but not ground-breaking. A restaurant switching its menu to only locally sourced ingredients is inspiring, but it won't save the planet. But getting a whole community of local food enterprises to start working together as part of a sustainable food system, now that really *can* have an impact. This is the founding theory of the Local Food Ecosystem.

Planning sustainable communities of the future

Until recently, food, and the way people would access it, fell completely outside the realm of planning departments. Even today most plans for significant new developments include no more than retail space (which will inevitably be filled by one of the major supermarkets), the obligatory provision for allotments, and if we're lucky, an open space which the developers tell us 'could be used as a farmers' market', as if there are hordes of market gardeners and artisanal food producers anxiously waiting for an opportunity to trade their wares within the yet to be established community.

There is an opportunity to do so much more than this.

An interesting avenue from which the Food Hub project has gained considerable traction is the development sector. In fact, I have been approached by several forward-thinking developers who are keen for the Food Hub to be located within their development. There appears to be an emerging trend in the house-building sector to try and create new communities in which people can experience high levels of well-being in a built environment designed to have low environmental impact. The visions for these communities usually discourage use of cars, and promote active lifestyles. They often include novel approaches to waste and water management, and extensively feature low-energy buildings. What is especially interesting, and exciting, about these new 'sustainable communities of the future' is the degree of planning that goes into their design at a strategic level; they are not simply collections of buildings, the planners and developers take an overview of the whole community, putting a lot of consideration into the *experience* of living and working within them, and what the overall environmental impact of these places will be. Sounds like the kind of place I would love to live myself.

The Local Food Ecosystem concept aligns really well with the exciting blue-skies thinking that is being applied to community design, and it is encouraging to see that certain developers have picked up on that. Having a Food Hub, or at least an outlet through which food sourced from the Local Food Ecosystem is available, will give the new community a sense of local identity, and contribute significantly towards placemaking. Members of the new community will not only have access to healthy locally and sustainably produced food, they can also obtain it in novel, energy-efficient and enjoyable ways. A Food Hub, and the incubator kitchens within it, would also bring employment opportunities to the new community, including ways of working that move away from the traditional '9 to 5' jobs and are better suited to modern lifestyles. Consider for a moment a stay-at-home parent who has moved to the new community. This person is passionate about baking, and dreams of running a business making cupcakes. Two days each week, after dropping the kids at school, they walk over to the Food Hub, where they have booked a flexible time slot in one of the kitchen units. They spend a few hours baking until it is time to leave and do the school pick-up run. Meanwhile, back at the Food Hub retail outlet, their cakes are selling like, well, 'hot cakes'.

I am particularly interested in the idea of there being less delineation regarding the purpose of public buildings. Conventionally our civic buildings serve a very specific purpose; a school is where people go for education, a supermarket is where people go to obtain food, and a church is where people go for matters of religion and community. But I am interested in the concept of having multi-purpose buildings. A Food Hub is not simply a place for food distribution, it should also be a place for community gatherings and activities, as well as food-related education and training.

Food is such a fundamentally important aspect of our lives and well-being, so it is encouraging to see that it is finally becoming a consideration when planning new communities. I'm extremely excited at the prospect of working with planners and developers at a strategic level, to work out how healthy and sustainable food integrates into these new sustainable communities and 'Healthy New Towns'.

17

What better education could you give a young person than knowledge about healthy and sustainable dietary choices and the skills to prepare food. Cambridge Sustainable Food provides cookery workshops for local families. On this occasion a group of children prepared and served a meal at Cambridge United Football club to guests including the club's chairman and players, and the mayor.

The purpose of this book

This book serves a dual purpose.

Firstly it is intended to provide the level of understanding about the Local Food Ecosystem that is so difficult to achieve in a pamphlet or an elevator pitch. It is a highly participatory system that functions better the more people engage with it. A Local Food Ecosystem that is functioning at its best will consist of many participants who have each interpreted the concept their own way, and engage with it not through altruism, but because they are realising genuine benefit for themselves and their enterprises. It is very important that the practitioners who participate in the system *understand* how the system is intended to function.

Secondly, and perhaps more importantly, this book is also about sharing a good idea: maybe inspiring others to initiate a Local Food Ecosystem in their own area, or perhaps even apply the concept to other types of industry. I am not precious about it. I don't want to keep it to myself as though it is some sort of 'secret formula'. Quite the opposite, in fact. If the Local Food Ecosystem concept really does have the potential to help the fight against climate change it would be irresponsible not to share it.

The Local Food Ecosystem works best when people take ownership of the concept for themselves, recognise their place in the system and make it work to their advantage. As you make your way through this book, try to think of yourself existing 'within' the Local Food Ecosystem, a *part* of it. What opportunities do you see for *yourself*? What ideas do *you* have? If you run or work for a food enterprise, would trading more easily with other local food businesses help make local food a prominent feature of your community, and how might your business prosper in the process?

In the next chapter I am going to further explore the philosophy underpinning the Local Food Ecosystem concept. I will talk about principles of Harmony and how they might be applied to business, not just food business but any sort of business, in order to create companies that conform to the 'new way' of doing things and are fit for the future.

In Chapters 3 and 4 I will go into the Local Food Ecosystem concept in further detail. In particular, I will describe the way that inputs can be balanced with outputs in order to minimise, and even eliminate, systemic wastage of food, and how food-delivery routes can be coordinated to minimise food miles at the macro and micro level.

And then in Chapter 5 I will explain how we can go about creating a Local Food Ecosystem. I will describe the business model for the Food Hub itself, and how it operates in order to support the functioning of the Local Food Ecosystem.

Finally, I will end the book by giving a vision of what the world might look like in the future, if the concept of the Local Food Ecosystem takes off. I will also describe the many benefits we could all experience when there is a vibrant Local Food Ecosystem functioning in our area.

The Local Food Ecosystem concept is a completely new food system. A re-structuring of supply chains. A new way for food businesses to trade with one another. An integrated framework of operations that works on the principles of balance, wholeness and interconnectivity. You have heard the slogan 'system change not climate change'; well this is what system change looks like.

What the Local Food Ecosystem means to me: Tristan Welch

When compiling this book I invited five food practitioners, each of whom performs a different role in the functioning of Cambridge's Local Food Ecosystem, to write an essay telling us about the concept from their own perspective. We start with Tristan Welch, chef and proprietor of one of Cambridge's most prestigious restaurants: Parker's Tavern. You may also recognise Tristan from TV shows such as *Saturday Kitchen* and *Snackmasters*. Here, Tristan tells us why choosing local ingredients is so important to him.

No place like home

Have you ever travelled long haul? I'm sure a lot of you have. Perhaps even halfway across the world to go on a holiday of a lifetime. If you are anything like me after a long-haul flight, you're not feeling your freshest, perhaps even past the sell-by date but hopefully not the use-by date! Like most of us, good food is better less travelled. Local produce, fresh from the source, is what I enjoy. It tastes better, it feels better, it's more nutritious so it's better for you, better for the local economy and the environment. Here my passion for local produce starts. It's the pursuit of the very best.

Sometimes our endeavours to better what we do take us further away from our intended goals.

I'm talking as a chef, and as chefs we constantly put ourselves under pressure to evolve our menus and the dishes within them, to offer our guests the very best we can. It's a race to stand out. During that race we sometimes miss what's right in front of us. What I found is that you don't have to look very far to find the very best and to stand out with a regionality that carves your menu and stimulates your creativity. There is a reason why the best Guinness only travels from Ireland to New York in hammocks! It just doesn't travel well, we don't travel well, our ingredients don't travel well. We might recover with time but our ingredients don't. A little bit of those ingredients dies with every mile they travel.

No matter where in the world I am, local ingredients is my passion, freshly picked and prepared. I remember my parents' garden and the treats that set a precedent for my future career. The sweet earthiness from the first of the season's potatoes and the sharp fruity rhubarbs to the richness of the eggs from the chickens. Magic like that just won't last for long but that's what I like to capture in the cooking at my restaurant. When I create a menu, it must be done hand in hand with Mother Nature.

For me asparagus sums it up really well. Asparagus comes once a year and it's something we all look forward to celebrating for the six-week season and then we forget what it tastes like for another 10 ½ months, until it comes again with the release of bottled-up excitement and we have a festival of flavours once again. British asparagus, often imitated never replicated, and that's what I love about local seasonal food. It's simply enjoyed while it's at its best and the absence only makes the heart grow fonder.

You can try dragging a mango across the world, I've tried it. Unless it has its own seat on the plane it just doesn't taste the same as it did at source. I can't eat bananas in this country any more after living in the Caribbean for many years and it breaks my heart. A banana ripened on a stem is just a beautiful sweet succulent thing; however, ripened on a boat it loses its life, vibrance and for me, sweetness. The interesting thing I saw was the community I lived with was just as keen on American/European items as the American/European countries were for the exotic treats from the island. Both parties shipping their finest to each other at the expense of quality.

To eat the very best, we need not look any further than our own back gardens, especially around here in East Anglia. The garden of the UK, I like to think.

Which leads me to regionality. What I hope for one day are little pockets around the UK, famously defined by specific ingredients that are exceptionally good and celebrated. In many ways that is already the case today, much like Kentish apples, Yorkshire rhubarb, samphire from Norfolk and brown shrimps from Kings Lynn. Unfortunately, as the world gets smaller we sadly lose the regionality through cheaper forgeries or from the loss of a suitable environment to grow. (How long has Champagne got before the climate will be unsuitable to grow vines?)

By dedicating myself to local produce and allowing Mother Nature, along with local purveyors, to guide me on what ingredients are at their best, I find myself put in a corner that spurs a fantastic stimulation of creativity. It inspires me to write my menus whilst keeping local regionality, quality, taste and guest experience at the forefront of mind. By utilising the best produce that's on our doorstep, we offer our guests a unique, regional and healthier experience in our restaurant.

When I started to look at local produce it took a while to adjust my eyes, much like mushroom picking. You have to find the first mushroom before you can find the others! Sure enough, much like mushrooms, once I started exploring what the local area has to offer, these local gems popped up everywhere. For example, pulses and grains that you would normally think grow in Italy and Asia grow in East Anglia! I also found poultry, game, cattle, asparagus, cheeses, beer, gin, sparkling wines, fruits from orchards and farms, and even the most delicious chilli peppers.

The wonderful thing is, if you're looking for the very best, quite often once you've adjusted your eyes you won't need to look very far.

When it comes down to it there's no place or taste quite like home.

Tristan Welch

Parker's Tavern restaurant sits within Cambridge's iconic University Arms Hotel.

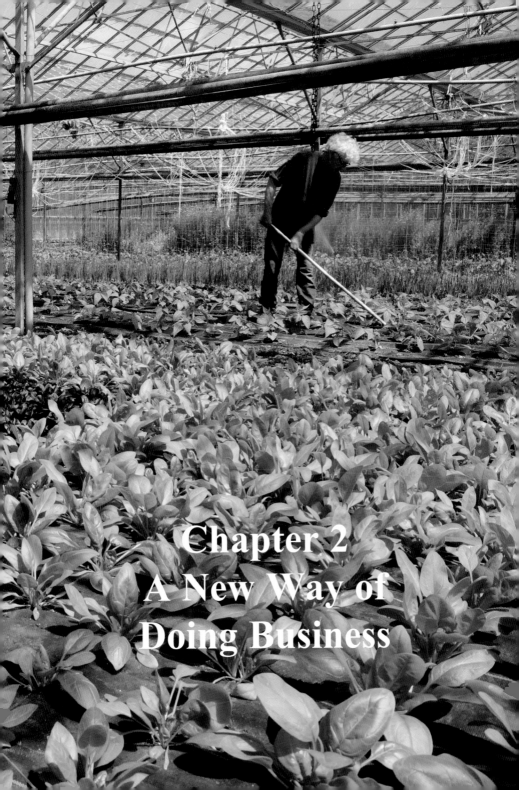

Chapter 2
A New Way of
Doing Business

Chapter 2
A New Way of Doing Business

To fully understand the concept for the Local Food Ecosystem it is important to understand the philosophy and principles that underpin it. In this chapter I am going to explain a little more about principles of Harmony, and how they might be applied to business and the economy.

To make a very general statement, many of the problems of the modern world exist because the world's economic model is out of tune with nature. The economists who are championing a 'new way' of doing things, and the pioneering businesses who are developing Circular Economy processes, envision a way of being in which we have a more harmonious relationship with the natural world and with each other.

The kind of businesses and industries that are right for the future, and will help us live more sustainably on this planet, are ones which either work completely in harmony with nature, without exploiting natural ecosystems but sustainably extracting resources from the environment, or they are systems which imitate or take inspiration from the way that natural systems manage materials and resources. Examples of the former of these would be a 'closed system' organic farm, a well-managed fishery or well-managed logging forest. The Local Food Ecosystem is an example of the latter, but this way of thinking could also be applied to all sorts of different industries. The terminology for describing such business systems hasn't really emerged yet, but the philosophy which underpins them is very much in line with that of the Harmony Project and the book *Harmony: A New Way of Looking at Our World*, mentioned in Chapter 1. So, for now at least, I'm going to call them 'Harmony businesses'.

For me, there are three main characteristics that would define a Harmony business:

- it would be founded on principles of Harmony
- it would have, as its primary objective, a 'noble purpose'

- it would deliver benefit to all of its stakeholders in equitable measure.

In this chapter I'm going to explore each of these characteristics

Principles of Harmony

To be clear, when I say that a Harmony business should be 'founded on principles of Harmony', what I mean is that the enterprise should be in tune with nature, respect ecological boundaries and take inspiration from nature in designing its processes.

It is an uncomfortable fact, but nearly all business, industrial and agricultural activity damages the environment to some extent, and this is causing climate change. 'Business as usual' simply isn't an option. Those of us who are interested in system change are not simply thinking about new environmentally friendly business ventures, but an entirely new way for business itself to be structured. Rethinking the role that business plays in society. Designing systems which are sustainable in the long term. The Harmony Project advocates creating systems, not just in business but in all arenas of human endeavour, which operate in harmony with natural systems, rather than in opposition to them.

Principles of Harmony is essentially an observation of the way that nature works, an interpretation of the Laws of Nature, if you like. I am sure many people, especially those indoctrinated in the Capital and Growth economic model, will find the notion of designing a business

An organic farm is an example of a business that operates completely in harmony with nature. This picture is of 'Permalogical' in Hertfordshire where some permaculture techniques are employed to produce food.

system based on nature to be whimsical nonsense. Well, let's dispel that attitude right away. Consider how our planet has a system that recycles and transports a *billion* tons of water every minute; how the rainforests are home to up to 50 *million* different species, some of which have synthesised compounds which could be used for the treatment of diseases such as cancer and HIV; how the evolutionary process has resulted in some amazing creatures, including ones with abilities such as flight and intelligence; how the sun continually provides the earth with *35,000 times* the amount of energy used by all human beings, and will continue to do so for 5 *billion* years. This is nature at work. These are astounding feats of design and engineering, compared to which the greatest achievements of mankind are almost insignificant. Nature is AWESOME. There's an awful lot for us to learn from nature if we have the humility to accept we are not its master. Looking to nature for inspiration when designing our businesses isn't a bad idea at all.

Some of the most important principles of Harmony that should be considered when designing our business systems are wholeness, interconnectivity, diversity, cycles, adaptability and balance. These principles do not merely manifest in nature, they are the very framework on which natural ecosystems are structured. I'm certainly not claiming for one moment that I *understand* how these principles work in nature; the interactions between the many millions of microscopic organisms in just one teaspoon of soil are incomprehensible, so how anyone could get their head around what's going on in a complex system like a rainforest is unimaginable. However, it is possible to envision how these principles could be applied to business, and perhaps by creating a framework for business according to these principles we will find that exciting and unpredicted efficiencies occur, or that new products and services emerge.

Looking to nature for inspiration when designing our businesses isn't a bad idea at all.

Everybody, and everything, is a part of a greater system, or **whole**. The great whole is itself made up of smaller systems, which can themselves be considered as whole. This is the principle of **wholeness**. There needs to be **diversity** within the whole: members who specialise in performing a specific role in the functioning of the system. Within the whole everybody and everything is linked, directly or indirectly, through interdependent relationships. Where there are relationships there are interactions, and, of course, the members of the system do not interact exclusively with just one other member. This is the principle of **interconnectivity.** These relationships exist in business just as they do in nature. Consider a clothing shop on the high street. This retail outlet is inextricably dependent on relationships with many other businesses. Its suppliers are an obvious one, but also energy companies, financial institutions, recruitment agencies, cleaning companies etc. Less directly, it is dependent on a multitude of other enterprises, not least every business or organisation which employs one of its customers and therefore provides the money that is eventually spent in the shop. Each of those businesses and organisations sits within its own network of interdependent relationships, of course, and eventually you end up with an all-encompassing whole in which there is an unfathomable nexus of dynamic connectedness.

The first step in applying principles of Harmony to your enterprise is simply to recognise that it is a whole, made up of its staff and assets, and that whole is part of a greater whole; the 'system' or 'industry' to which it belongs. Any notion of 'independence' or that you have any form of control over the system is a fallacy, and this is just as true in the Capital and Growth way as it would be in the Nature and Harmony way; a supplier might stop supplying you due to pressure from one of your more influential competitors, and we've seen famous examples of when product reformulations have met with resistance from customers, forcing a return to the original recipe.[4] It is important to understand your role within the functioning of the whole and the value that you bring to it. Get this right, and deliver that value well and consistently, and you have a firm foundation for business success.

A prosperous 'whole' equates to prosperity for *all* of its constituent parts. It is in the interests of each member of the system to ensure that

---

4. 'New Coke'.

their fellow members are doing well. It seems like common sense that it would be good for a company if all the other companies that it traded with were in good shape themselves. Yet so often the Capital and Growth mindset does not see it this way; this is apparent in the food industry where the tendency is for larger companies to systematically worsen trading terms with their suppliers, not only with price, but also credit terms, and power balance. This process can be devastating for farmers. A less obvious application of this principle is considering the welfare of a member of the whole that you do not have a direct relationship with, or even one whose interests are seemingly in conflict with your own, such as a competitor. A café owner may, seemingly, have no association whatsoever with the bookshop three streets away, but that bookshop is part of the draw which brings visitors to the town centre, who enjoy sitting down for a cup of coffee in the afternoon. As for a competitor, well, the principle still applies. Whereas our café owner probably has an indifferent attitude towards the bookshop, and is perfectly happy to see them do well and help them out when they can, they probably have a very different opinion of the new café which opens on the other side of the street. Counterintuitively, the prosperity of this new café also impacts the prosperity of the original one. The presence of two cafés in close proximity means the area gains a reputation for being the place to go for cafés, and as each competes with the other for custom, their product offering improves and they develop as a business. The natural instinct in business is to want to suppress competition; however, learning to accept and embrace it is a far healthier attitude.

The prosperity of the whole in nature is achieved either through mutually beneficial interactions, or interactions which may not apparently benefit one party directly, but comes back to benefit them some other way; the individual acquiesces to the ecosystem, and the ecosystem takes care of the individual. Interactions in a business context usually means transactions. One way to achieve prosperity of the whole in a business system is to make sure that transactions are always fair; both parties deriving benefit for themselves in equitable measure. This is where the ideology of the Harmony business diverges from the Capital and Growth approach to business relationships, where the attitude is one of competitiveness; a win–lose scenario where one party, usually the one with greater power and control, makes sure they get the better deal. In a harmonious economy all deals should be win–win. Another way to achieve unanimous prosperity throughout the whole is through 'right relationships'. What are right relationships? Well, I'd say these are relationship built on qualities such as trust, respect and kindness. We should never forget that the people who work in business are, first and foremost, *people*. Business should exist to serve people, not the other way round. Personally I always respond much better, and feel as though my needs have been better met, when I have been treated with kindness in business, and the same is just as true when I feel I have been kind to someone else.

> *Business should exist to serve people, not the other way round.*

In nature *everything* is recycled. At school we learnt about the water cycle, the nitrogen cycle, the cycling of carbon dioxide and oxygen through respiration and photosynthesis. Natural ecosystems operate on a continuous cycle of birth, death and decomposition. Nature operates according the circular rhythms of the seasons, themselves dictated by the circular journey the earth makes around the sun. The principle of **cycles**

We have a lot to learn from nature. Giving children experiences and education in natural environments is essential if we are to transition to a 'new way' of doing things which is in Harmony with nature.

32

is the one that has resonated most prominently with exponents of the 'new way' of doing things, particularly the Circular Economy, because it is here that we see the most obvious contrast between the way things are currently being done and the way we know they must be done: between the destructive and the regenerative. A linear economy is almost entirely founded on the exploitation of natural resources through activities like mining (for fossil fuels and other minerals or metals), over-fishing, intensive agriculture and deforestation. But we know that these resources are all finite; there is only so much oil in the ground and there is no way to revive a species once it has become extinct.

Circular-economy theory prescribes that we extract maximum value from the resources that are already available to us and leave the untapped ones where they should be; in the ground. For material goods this means extracting maximum value from them by keeping them in their 'high value' state for as long as possible, repairing, restoring, sharing, reselling, and when the item has truly reached the end of its useful lifespan, recycling the materials it was made from. For natural resources, such as food, water, wood and renewable energy, it means using no more than nature can afford to let us have without compromising its regenerative capabilities. And we shouldn't be apprehensive about that; nature is a very generous and abundant provider and there should be enough for everyone as long as sensible patterns of consumption are observed.

The principle of **adaptability** refers to the ability of an individual, or a system, to be able to adjust to a change in circumstances. This is an incredibly important quality to have in terms of the resilience of a system. The adaptability of various industries was put to the test recently by the coronavirus pandemic. Smaller, independent businesses were able to respond and adapt to the lockdown much faster than the larger ones. While supermarkets struggled for several weeks to cope with panic buying and the change in purchasing habits to home-delivery, many small, local food businesses reacted quickly and adapted to the change, often also responding in a socially responsible manner which ensured that vulnerable people could access food. The Cambridge Organic Food Company is a great example; existing members of the box scheme experienced no disruption to their service whatsoever, and within three weeks systems and infrastructure had all been adapted to enable a doubling in capacity. I know the same to be true of box schemes and Food Hubs up and down the country.

The final principle I am going to talk about is **balance**. Nowhere in nature does an individual take more than is necessary for its own survival or accumulate resources beyond what can be managed by themselves. Were this to happen it would inevitably upset the balance of nature and disrupt the functioning of the ecosystem. If lions killed more than their fair share of grazing animals this would not only diminish the sustainability of their food source, it would also mean the ungrazed land would become forest, thereby diminishing their habitat as well. Instead, the lions, grazing animals and grassland exist in a state of dynamic equilibrium, keeping each other's numbers in check and maintaining the balance of the ecosystem. The same is true at all levels of the ecosystem.

A problem with profit, or more specifically the point at which exploitation-derived profit is extracted from the system, is that it causes imbalance.

Most linear business processes exploit a natural resource at some point along the chain (usually the beginning). Obvious examples include wood from deforestation, fish from over-fishing or oil from drilling, but other significant ways in which the natural world is exploited include exhausting soil fertility, or polluting the atmosphere with greenhouse gases and waterways with nitrites. People are exploited as well. Sometimes directly, through underpaid labour, or indirectly through the many forms of ill health that are associated with industrialisation. This exploitation is extremely costly, in ecological terms, societal terms and financial terms, but these costs do not appear on the company's balance sheet: they are externalised costs. The capital generated at the other end of the chain, the 'profit', is not really profit at all. It is not value that has been created, it is value that has been taken; profit derived from exploitation. A resource which is being exploited will eventually be exhausted. This is, by definition, unsustainable. In every sense this mechanism causes imbalance: financial imbalance, natural imbalance and an imbalance in power.

OK, I am well aware that the last section may be contentious, especially among the readers of this book who are small-business owners and whose livelihood is dependent upon that very marginal and difficult to obtain segment of their company's finances which is 'profit'. Please do read on. By the end of this chapter you will understand the distinction between profit derived from exploitation and 'sustainable profit', and how a business founded on principles of Harmony can be a highly successful and rewarding enterprise.

The organic kitchen garden at Audley End House.

Survival of the fittest?

There is a popular misconception that nature is harsh, brutal and gruelling. It is 'eat or be eaten', 'survival of the fittest'.

Capital and Growth businesses often use this kind of rhetoric, and behave accordingly. The 'bigger fish' consume the 'smaller fish', either through acquisitions and mergers or by putting them out of business, until you end up with mega corporations with huge amounts of power and control. In doing so they may well believe they have behaved according to the natural order of things.

This interpretation of 'survival of the fittest' depicts nature as if it were some kind of 'Hunger Games'-style contest, where all participants battle to be the sole remaining survivor. But this isn't what nature is like at all. This would be a move away from **diversity** for starters, and one thing we can say unequivocally about nature is that it is characterised by mind-blowing levels of biodiversity.

'Survival of the fittest' is a term that comes from the theory of evolution. It refers to reproductive success and the passing on of genetic traits that are best adapted to the environment, ensuring that the species in question is best equipped to perform its role in the functioning of the **whole**. It is not about a battle for ultimate dominance. The competition isn't against each other, the competition is for personal betterment.

Perhaps what I am trying to explain is better understood if we stop thinking about an ecosystem being made up of 'individuals', but instead made up of 'components'. A component might be a species or a group of species which perform a similar role in the functioning of the ecosystem. While life can indeed be very harsh for many individuals, the ecosystem is an incredibly hospitable place for its components. This is cold comfort for the tadpole (an individual) which gets eaten up by a dragonfly larva, but frogs in general (the component) continue to be a successful species, and those frogs exist in **balance** with the many other species that constitute the ecosystem.

In business, companies are not individuals, they are *components* of the system. A prosperous business ecosystem would consist of many diverse companies who have each used the theory of 'survival of the fittest' to become robust businesses who fulfil their role in the system very well, not one or two companies who have displaced all others. In nature, the individual, such as the unfortunate tadpole in the earlier example, is a resource which is exchanged with the rest of the ecosystem, the equivalent of which in the business world, therefore, would be products.

The 'noble purpose' of a business, and how profit compromises its delivery

All industries should have, as their primary objective, a 'noble purpose'. This is the product or service provided which brings *genuine* benefit to people and society. It is the value which is brought to the whole.

The noble purpose of a good company will become its 'mission statement', and therefore the 'stone of truth' which guides the direction and the decision making of the company. Please understand the distinction between a 'noble purpose' and a 'mission statement', for while all noble purposes are mission statements, not all mission statements are noble purposes. A company whose mission was to cut down every tree in the Amazon rainforest and turn the land into intensive cattle feedlots would not have a noble purpose.

Most Capital and Growth companies have profit as their primary objective and this inevitably leads to a distortion in the way that people's needs are met and the way problems are solved. To understand what I mean, follow me through this thought exercise …

Start by describing what might appear to be the most obvious observation about the purpose of a company or industry, perhaps in the way a child may see it:

'The purpose of the car industry is to make cars.'

OK, let's go a little deeper and think about *why* it is making those cars. What is the benefit being brought to society and the problem being solved?

The purpose of the car industry is to provide people with a means of transporting themselves and their goods from one place to another.'

We can easily turn this into a noble purpose by adding a dimension that considers its long-term sustainability:

'The purpose of the car industry is to provide people with a means of transporting themselves and their goods from one place to another in an energy-efficient way with minimal environmental impact.'

Of course, this isn't the primary objective of the car industry at all. The primary objective of the car industry is to make money.

If the motor industry had set out from the beginning with this noble purpose, the cars we would be driving today would look very different, if they were even cars at all. In fact, the whole transport infrastructure and our way of life would be radically different to what has now become the

norm. The presence of profit as the primary motivation of this industry has dramatically influenced the way it has gone about solving the problem of personal transportation, and this means we have ended up with something which is less efficient and less beneficial to society and environment than it might otherwise have been. Having profit as the primary motivation of the car industry has been counter-productive to achieving its noble purpose.

The same is just as true with the food industry. To my mind there is a noble purpose for the food industry which just seems so obvious and right: *'The purpose of the food industry is feeding people, with healthy and sustainably produced food.'*

But, of course, this isn't the primary objective of the mainstream food industry. Its primary objective is profit. Here, again, having profit as the primary objective has influenced the way the industry has gone about achieving its purpose. Maximising profit inevitably leads to unsustainable farming practices and diminished nutritional value of food, with unequal distribution of it. If you took the, very reasonable, purpose statement above and used it as a benchmark for measuring the performance of the food industry then it would be judged to be performing very poorly indeed: millions of people are hungry, so it is not feeding people; there is a prevalence of food products with poor nutritional quality, so it is not healthy; and most mainstream food production degrades soils and is reliant on fossil fuels, so it is not sustainable. Having profit as the primary motivation of the food industry is extremely counter-productive.

Now, just because profit isn't the *primary* objective of an industry doesn't mean it cannot be *an* objective. Profit in and of itself isn't a bad thing. The notion of adding value to materials, or providing services and being paid money in return, is fundamentally a good thing; it is value that has been created as a results of people's skills and labour and it's how people carve out a living for themselves. The point I am trying to make isn't that profit should be eliminated, just that there are other objectives which are more important. We need to reorder the priorities of our companies so that they are able to operate for the greater good rather than being restricted by an unsophisticated mindset which insists that profits must be maximised above all else (sometimes even to the detriment of the company itself). I quite like the slogan that some social enterprises use: 'People before Profit'. This slogan doesn't deny the significance of profit, it simply states that people are more important. It is such accepted wisdom that a company exists primarily to make money for its shareholders, and that the products and services it provides are merely the mechanism by which it does this. But if you think about it, this is just nuts. The products and services provided by these companies are such an important aspect of the everyday lives of people, shouldn't provision of those products and services be the most important thing that a company does? Why can't a business be allowed to just do what it is meant to do? Why must it always have to pander to an arbitrary, alternative purpose? Freed from the shackles of having to maximise profitability at every opportunity, a company can go ahead and perform its operations in the way that best meets the needs of the community it serves. Behaving this way results in a company that is far more valuable to society, and therefore more successful.

I feel that here I need to qualify the use of the terms 'success' and 'successful' throughout this book. Many people's immediate response to these words is an association with the accumulation of wealth; perhaps evidence of the extent to which Capital and Growth is ingrained in our consciousness. To my mind, the word 'success' means achieving goals and meeting objectives. The objectives of a Harmony business are much more elaborate than simply the pursuit of wealth. The use of the term at the end of the last paragraph referred to success across a range of objectives, including financial success.

Attaching profit to the product or service being provided, and especially having profit as the primary motivation for that product or service, usually means that the product or service is not being delivered in the best, most efficient or fairest way. However, no enterprise can deliver products and services without generating revenue to cover its operational costs. One way in which an organisation *can* deliver its products and services in the best, most efficient and fairest way possible is to keep the operational costs distinct from the provision of those products or services. An example of this is the way that the BBC is funded. The purchase of a TV licence is completely distinct from the activity of watching television. The BBC covers its operational costs through licence fees which means it can carry out its operations without compromise. As a result, the BBC is able to produce very high-quality content, its service is delivered equitably throughout the community (including free or reduced-rate provision of services for people who only want to listen to the radio, the elderly, or visually-impaired people), it is excellent value for money compared to subscription-based television, and the customer's experience is in no way compromised by other commercial influences (i.e. you don't have to watch adverts). The noble purpose of the BBC is: *'to act in the public interest, serving all audiences through the provision of impartial, high-quality and distinctive output and services which inform, educate and entertain.'* And it does this very well through virtue of keeping its revenue stream separate from its operational activity.

Equitable measure

For me, the benchmark of a really good business would be this: *a business that is capable of providing value to its owners, staff, customers, suppliers, society and the environment in equitable measure.*

The most important aspect of this premise is that *all* stakeholders derive at least some benefit from that activity of the business. Most Capital and Growth businesses function by exploiting at least one of these stakeholder groups for the benefit of another. There are many examples of companies where the owners benefit disproportionately to the other stakeholder groups, and in the worst cases exploit ALL of their stakeholders for the benefit of the owners (I shan't name names). More often than not, it is the environment that gets the raw end of the deal, and this is something we're *all* guilty of. Virtually all businesses have at least some form of fossil-fuel energy use somewhere in their supply chain. It is virtually impossible to operate any other way within the current economic paradigm. Even The Cambridge Organic Food Company isn't beyond reproach; some of our produce arrives in diesel vehicles and we have a cold-store which uses a lot of electricity (although we will have addressed the latter once the Cambridge Food Hub building is complete).

The Hallmark of a really good business would be one that is capable of providing value to its owners, staff, customers, suppliers, society and the environment in equitable measure.

Just imagine how great a company would be if it did indeed meet this benchmark. For starters it would be great for the planet, and it would set a fantastic precedent for businesses to stop damaging the environment and work for its benefit instead. Secondly, bear in mind that this operation benefits *all* of its stakeholders. This would be a company that maintains mutually rewarding relationships with a multitude of people and other enterprises, each of whom not only values its existence from their own perspective, but appreciates the value it brings to the whole to which they belong. This company would be *loved* by its staff, its customers, its suppliers and the community. And something which is loved can endure, grow and *succeed*.

There are many much more authentic ways of measuring success other than profit. All the same, the company just described would indeed include profit among its many successes, and this is where the reasoning about profit throughout this chapter comes full circle: for all profit generated by this company is 'sustainable profit'. None of the company's stakeholder groups have been exploited; they have all received their fair share of the proceeds, so there is no 'profit derived from exploitation'. Let's not forget that one of the stakeholder groups that benefits is the owners. If this company were delivering massive benefit to its staff, customers, suppliers, society and the environment it would also be delivering massive benefit to its owners. This is good news for the prospects of creating new Harmony businesses as people are much more likely to start one or invest in one if they can see clear benefit in doing so, although this does come with a precautionary note: remember that extracting profit from the system causes imbalance. In an enterprise, profit enables the company or industry to grow (and if the company is doing good things then that's great), it can help reward suppliers or staff, or it could enable the company to perform altruistic deeds that benefit society or the environment. Profit only becomes bad when it undermines the noble purpose of the industry, or when it causes imbalance in the system. I'm afraid that in a harmonious economy there is no place for opulence; investing in a Harmony business is not something you should do if you aspire to own a Lamborghini, a Learjet or a second home in St Lucia. But then again, these status symbols are only really coveted by those who are still indoctrinated in the Capital and Growth mindset. When you think about it, there is very little that a person can spend their disposable income on which isn't inherently bad for the planet, yet another quandary of the Capital and Growth system. Letting go of the desire to acquire more and more goods can be incredibly liberating. Owners of Harmony businesses can indeed expect to benefit greatly from them, but bear in mind that there are other measures of benefit and success than simply the financial.

Conclusion

Creating a business model that doesn't have profit as its core objective will seem completely alien, ludicrous even, to anyone who is indoctrinated into the Capital and Growth way. However, 'business as usual' is proving itself to be highly unsustainable. A business that prioritises purpose over profitability, and operates within ecological boundaries in harmony with nature, will not only bring benefits to a wide range of stakeholders but be capable of creating sustainable profit as well. Counterintuitive as it may sound, business owners and investors are better off this way; a modest return, reliably sustained indefinitely from a robust and sustainable business which reinvests and grows, is much better than the short-term gratification of big pay-outs from a company whose business model is fundamentally unsustainable. And business is a competitive world; any company which places its noble purpose higher than profit on its objectives list is going to be better at providing value to society and more fit for purpose than its profit-motivated rivals. Ultimately, the purpose-driven enterprise will win.

The key take-home from this particular chapter is that if you focus first and foremost on the noble purpose of your business enterprise, and build a company around that, then you will end up with something which brings true benefit to a number of stakeholders. Get this right and the profit will follow. And these types of businesses should not be considered as 'niche'. Far from it. Linear business models have a finite lifespan; in fact, they may already have passed their peak. Harmony businesses are resilient and sustainable. Harmony is the business of the future.

What the Local Food Ecosystem means to me: Rosie Sykes

Rosie Sykes is a chef and food writer. As well as working in many renowned restaurants, Rosie has also volunteered for several social food projects that prepare meals for people who might need them, including the Square Food Foundation in Bristol. She plans to start a similar initiative in Cambridge. Here, Rosie tells us about her attitude towards surplus food.

The concept of 'waste' food is one that is unfortunately very much part of the food chain at the moment and something that a lot of people are trying hard to address and find solutions to. It is regrettable that we find ourselves in such a situation. It is estimated that about one third of food produced worldwide is wasted. We should all be doing our bit to stop this from happening.

One part of this chain which is of great interest is the repurposing of surplus (which would probably otherwise be considered waste). It should not be looked upon as a problem but as a positive element of the food chain that can be used for good.

Fresh food is not always accessible to everybody and it should be a basic human right. People's attitude to food changed after WWII when rationing kept a lot of the country in a state of near hunger. After this dark and difficult period, the industrialisation of food began and convenience and cut-price food became the name of the game. As our culture became more and more 'throw away' so did the approach to food and its procurement, until we got to the point we are at now when a call to arms about sustainability and ecological credentials urged more and more people to practise less wasteful food systems at home and in business.

Waste has negative connotations and so the term surplus seems like a better one to use. This is how I see food within our local food ecosystem that hasn't found a home and my hope is to be able to use it for good and close this particular supply circle. Surplus food can include vegetables that may be past their prime, but may also include items that are in perfect condition but for whatever reason may not have been needed.

The first category are usually quite serviceable but may take more time to prepare, picking through less good produce, and although there will be some legitimate waste it is less than if the whole lot had been consigned to the bin. There are now organisations which collect items in the second category and redistribute them to good causes – like charities that may use them to make up food parcels for those in need or may turn them into food for people on the breadline. My aim is to use surplus food, notably to feed those in need, but to fund all the workings of feeding people below the breadline by catering for local businesses, either by providing lunches for employees or food for conferences, working meals or events within the local food economy.

Throughout the pandemic of 2020 from March to August I took on a voluntary role cooking for about 200 financially insecure people in the local area. They were mainly the families of children who would normally receive free school meals. A friend and I were offered a small amount of funding by a private benefactor and the free use of the premises of a local restaurant which was closed during lockdown. Foodwise, my first port of call was the local Food Hub and Duncan himself because, knowing him as I do, I knew he would understand our plight and want to help, and having used produce from him for many years I was very aware of the quality and credentials, and of the fact that by using up the surplus from the Hub for social enterprise purposes I would be providing a good link in the local food economy – a joining-up if you like.

As a chef of many years standing I have carved out my own kind of cooking, and one of my passions is to be given things that need using and being able to make creative, delicious food from them. This is where I see waste becoming an asset. I would very much like to be able to inspire people to take my point of view and do the same.

Teaching people to cook is very much about inspiring and nurturing confidence in those learning to go off with some new skills and a wish to experiment and find their own groove. I think it is very possible with some encouragement and some general basic principles we could see the use of surplus becoming part of our food culture.

Food education is not widely available in a coherent fashion in schools at the moment but it should be, and it is by guiding the young that we should hope to be able to have a stronger basis for attaining a more sustainable food economy in local communities.

In conclusion, in an ideal world there would be little or no surplus or waste food. We are not at that point yet but if we can catch the food before it is too late and use it for good in the knowledge that that will sometimes take a little more time and work than the slightly unreal 'perfect' produce we are accustomed to in supermarkets, we could be making a step towards optimising the way we see and use food.

Rosie Sykes

During the coronavirus lockdown Rosie Sykes led a team of volunteers preparing free meals for vulnerable people, using donated surplus produce as their ingredients.

Chapter 3
The Local Food
Ecosystem in Theory

Chapter 3
The Local Food Ecosystem in Theory

Before I start to describe the Local Food Ecosystem I'd like you to take a moment or two to think about what you think an ideal food system would look like. Please literally do this ... before starting the next paragraph just sit back and reflect upon what, in *your* opinion, would constitute a really positive and vibrant local food economy. What would you like the food system in *your* area to be like?

Chances are, what you have just envisioned is pretty close to what I would describe as a Local Food Ecosystem, and there are two reasons why I think this is a safe bet. The first of these is based on the assumptions I have made about you, the reader, simply through virtue of the fact that you are reading a book of this subject matter. I think it is likely that you fall into one of the following categories: you may be a 'food practitioner' (your vocation is food, e.g. you are a farmer, or you own or work for a food business); you are somehow involved in food policy or environmental action in your area (maybe you work in government, food or environmental research, or are a volunteer in a local action group – someone I might bump into at an event such as the Sustainable Food Places Conference); or you are a citizen who takes a keen interest in food sustainability and wider environmental issues. By and large, there does seem to be a consensus on the type of thing people like you and I want the food system in their area to be like: a proliferation of locally grown fresh produce which comes directly from local farms, a plethora of artisanal food businesses providing an abundance of delicious foods, good food being within reach of all members of the community (when I say 'within reach' I mean both literally, by being available from a shop that is within walking distance from your home, and figuratively, meaning it is not being marketed to a specific segment of the community, i.e. the affluent), and a food system which is kinder to the environment.

The other reason why I believe you thought up something which is close to the vision of the Local Food Ecosystem is because what you envisaged will, quite literally, go on to influence the identity of the Local Food Ecosystem in your area. As you will read later in this chapter, one of the features of the Local Food Ecosystem is that it is egalitarian; moulded by the will of its collective membership. The Local Food Ecosystem in your area will be an aggregation of what you came up with when you did the earlier thought exercise and the ideas of other practitioners and consumers of food in your area. It is not for me to dictate what type of food system is 'right' in any particular area, that vision needs to come from the people who are of that area.

What is a Local Food Ecosystem?

A Local Food Ecosystem consists of all sorts of food enterprises within a geographical area: farmers (both large scale and small), food-processing businesses, independent retailers, restaurants and cafés, catering businesses, schools and colleges, organisations who make food more accessible to deprived segments of the community. Basically, anyone whose livelihood somehow involves food. These are the 'members' of the Local Food Ecosystem.

Of course, every town and city already has a community of local food enterprises. This pre-existing community of food enterprises is what we might call a local food network. So, what is the difference between this and the new concept I am describing? When does a local food network become a Local Food Ecosystem?

The distinction between a local food network and a Local Food Ecosystem is the way the members of the system interact with one another and the way the supply chain is managed. In a Local Food Ecosystem the interactions and connections between local food enterprises are far more widespread. There is a collective understanding that the members of the Local Food Ecosystem should trade with one another whenever possible, and that acting in unity with one another creates a significant sector within the local market which is able to hold its own against competition from industrialised food. This results in a burgeoning local economy in which independent food businesses can really prosper. The main difference between a local food network and a Local Food Ecosystem is that of scale;

The Cambridge Loaf is a delicious sourdough bread that resulted from a collaboration between a local farm, a local miller and a local baker. Collaborations between local growers and local food processing enterprises will be commonplace in a Local Food Ecosystem.

it would be like comparing a collection of stalls at a village fete to the Grand Bazaar in Istanbul.

But the benefits of the Local Food Ecosystem do not end there, there is much more to the concept than simply that ...

When the number of local enterprises involved, and the number of interactions between them, reaches a critical mass this enables some very special techniques of food supply chain coordination to take place. These techniques enable a number of environmental and social benefits to come into effect: specifically eliminating systemic food waste, improving access to healthy food, a considerable reduction in food miles, enabling the cycling of surplus or waste, and implementing returnable/reusable packaging schemes. These techniques are detailed in the next chapter. These techniques also provide the members of the Local Food Ecosystem with a considerable competitive advantage, because they not only reduce their costs, but also endow their products with a compelling selling point that appeals to the growing consumer demand for products with high ethical ratings.

In the Local Food Ecosystem the supply chain is structured according the principles of Harmony that we discussed in the previous chapter. The Local Food Ecosystem considers the food system as a **whole**, and **balances** the needs of a diverse range of food enterprises in a way that achieves many social and environmental benefits. The system operates on the basis of vastly improved **connectivity** between its members, and managing resources in **circular** processes.

For the Ecosystem to function properly it needs to have representation from each of the aforementioned enterprise types. And it also needs to have active participation from a good number of local enterprises. The more the merrier. The benchmarks for determining that you have a functioning Local Food Ecosystem are if the members feel that they are part of something greater than themselves, and also feel that they are better off being a part of the Ecosystem than they would be otherwise.

Hot Numbers is a great example of a successful independent business in Cambridge. Proprietor Simon Fraser runs three coffee shops, the flagship of which is in their 'roastery', where they also roast coffee and bake bread.

The Local Food Ecosystem considers the food system as a whole, and balances the needs of a diverse range of food enterprises in a way that achieves many social and environmental benefits.

There will be people who are reading this and thinking that their area has a pretty good local food system already. Take Cambridge for example; there is ample opportunity for anyone living here to obtain fresh, local organic produce from a number of independent shops, from the Sunday market or from one of the farmers' markets that regularly take place. They could join The Cambridge Organic Food Company box scheme, of course, or there is a fantastic community-supported agriculture scheme called Cropshare which takes place at Waterland Organics. There is a number of superb artisanal bakeries and micro-breweries in and around the city. There is a fantastic street food and restaurant scene too. All in all, if you are a lover of good food you are not going to be disappointed by what Cambridge has to offer. But this isn't even close to what a fully functioning Local Food Ecosystem would be like. Let's get things into perspective; The Cambridge Organic Food Company is a thriving local organic veg box business, but there are *twenty-six* branches of Tesco within the same geographical area of business, the largest of which probably turns over in a week what COFCO manages in a year. And that is only one chain of supermarkets, of course. The Cambridge Organic Food Company reaches less than 1 per cent of the population of the area. Make no mistake: sustainable, local food is an extremely niche market at present. The vision for the Local Food Ecosystem is for this marvellous food to be ubiquitous, for it to become a normal feature of everyday life for a lot of people. Instead of 1 or 2 per cent of the market being taken up by local and sustainable food, it should be 20 or 30 per cent, or even more. There should be an independent food shop within walking distance of your home where you will find an abundant range of fresh fruits and vegetables which have come directly from local farms, as well as a range of processed foods which have also been made locally from local produce. When you pop out of work at lunchtime to get a sandwich, or when you go out for a meal in the evening, you should be spoilt for choice for delis, cafés and restaurants which are all using fresh local produce as their ingredients. When you send your kids to school you should be confident that they will be getting a nutritious meal made from fresh, local food.

In summary, the term 'Local Food Ecosystem' describes a community of local food enterprises which interact with one another in accordance with this new concept for food supply chain coordination. This concept includes some specific techniques which help minimise food waste, reduce emissions in the supply chain, and ensure that food is distributed more equitably in the community. These techniques are described in the following chapter, but for now I am going to expand on the theory of the Local Food Ecosystem.

Why the term 'ecosystem'?

The Local Food Ecosystem was conceived as an alternative food distribution system in which the many problems that manifest in linear food supply systems do not exist. This new system has been designed to incorporate principles of Harmony at the most fundamental level.

One way in which a business process can be designed to be more harmonious with nature is to draw inspiration from nature itself, and try to emulate natural processes in a business context. In the case of the Local Food Ecosystem, the term 'ecosystem' has purposefully been used because the way resources are managed in this concept emulates the way resources are used in a natural ecosystem, and the way enterprises interact with each other emulates the way components of a natural ecosystem interact with each other.

I have already talked about principles such as balance, diversity, wholeness, adaptability, interconnectivity and circularity, but what does this actually mean? In our theoretical model of the Local Food Ecosystem how are these principles implemented, and what benefits does that bring?

One important characteristic of a natural ecosystem, and one which would be desirable to emulate in a business process, is that nothing goes to waste. In fact, the whole concept of waste is completely alien in the natural world. This, then, is one of the significant benefits brought about by the Local Food Ecosystem that sets it apart from linear food supply chains: *everything* **finds a destination where it is valued and nothing goes to waste.**

The concept of waste is completely alien in the natural world.

The two principles which are particularly relevant when it comes to waste, or, more importantly, its prevention, are circularity and interconnectedness. In nature *all* resources are 'cycled'. Water, nutrients, minerals, gases; anything which is a surplus or by-product from one component of the ecosystem inevitably becomes the raw materials of life for another. The functioning of a natural ecosystem involves a web of interactions between its component organisms of such complexity it is beyond human comprehension. It is through interconnectedness that resources are used so efficiently in a natural ecosystem, and so it is that interconnectedness leads to more efficient use of resources and elimination of waste in the Local Food Ecosystem. **A fundamental principle of the Local Food Ecosystem concept is improved connectivity between its members.** In business terms, connections usually (but not exclusively) means transactions: a farmer selling some carrots to a local shop for example. In the Local Food Ecosystem we want these interactions to be as widespread as possible, and not just going in a single direction either. The farmer might also sell some carrots to a local soup manufacturer, who purchases some of their other ingredients from the same shop the farmer supplies, and that soup is also sold to the shop. The more interactions there are, the greater the likelihood that a resource will find its way to the destination where it is most valued.

Better connectivity is achieved in the Local Food Ecosystem through the provision of local distribution infrastructure. This is something we will come on to in later chapters. When this infrastructure exists there is much greater opportunity for resources to be **cycled**. Members of the Local Food Ecosystem are encouraged to be fanatical about making sure that any 'valuable' resources that they do not need find their way to another member of the Ecosystem rather than going in the bin. 'Valuable' was put in inverted commas here because the types of resources I am talking about here do not necessarily have *monetary* value, but they almost certainly have value, nonetheless. I am talking about things like unsold food, compostable waste, and empty, reusable packaging. In the 'linear' supply chains which currently exist the cost of collecting and transporting these resources usually outweighs the benefit of doing it, and so they end up in the bin instead. In the Local Food Ecosystem these resources can be efficiently transported to someone who would be pleased to accept them: a homeless shelter that is grateful for food donations, a farmer who can compost the waste, or a jam-maker who would make good use of some empty jars. Cycling materials in this way does happen at present, but only at 'cottage industry' scale. In the Local Food Ecosystem these processes become an integral part of the system, and happen on a much more significant scale.

The term Local Food Ecosystem implies inclusivity: a **diverse** web of food enterprises, covering all aspects of the food chain, in which all are welcome and which becomes stronger and more resilient the more members it attracts. As has already been said, every area already has its own 'local food network', comprising the very enterprises just described. So the term 'ecosystem' also implies that the members of the system engage with each other as if they are part of something greater: the **whole**. The prosperity of the whole has a direct correlation with the prosperity of its component parts. The more an enterprise interacts with the Ecosystem, the more they will get out of it for themselves. A farmer should be encouraged to sell their produce first to other members of the Ecosystem, and retailers and restaurants should likewise be encouraged to buy as much as they can from local producers. Of course, in business 'encouragement' *has* to mean some form of commercial advantage. In a prosperous Local Food Ecosystem there are many commercial advantages which make local trade an obvious choice. There is a financial one: in the Local Food Ecosystem trade is direct and many of the costs incurred through lengthy supply chains and transportation have been eliminated. There is a marketing one: as consumers become increasingly conscientious about social and environmental issues the 'ethical spend' will be on local and sustainable goods. And there is a social one: if you are performing a role that is of value to your community then the community itself will rally together to support you, especially in times of need. This so-called 'social capital' or 'community capital' shouldn't be overlooked. As I've said before, there is a 'human' element to this; there is no rule that says being in business means you can't be friendly, and the quality of life of everyone in business improves when those interactions are kind and loving. Just because 'quality of life' doesn't have a price attached to it, doesn't mean it isn't valuable, or, indeed, important.

A team of volunteer pickers help out in an organic apple orchard. There are many types of work done by people throughout society which is not accounted for financially. This 'social capital' is a vital part of our economy.

The value of the entrepreneur

Through the process of writing, re-reading and editing this book I am struck by how remarkably 'left-wing' it all sounds; all this talk about profit being counter-productive and egalitarian governance structures. I meant everything I have said, of course; I've been contemplating these issues and ideas extensively, and have concluded that a food system driven by Capital and Growth ideals just isn't fit for the future. At the same time, you have to bear in mind that for the past twenty-odd years I have been running a 'for-profit' business, with an autocratic governance system. You have to bear in mind that the majority of members of Local Food Ecosystems are also *businesses*. You have to bear in mind that the most significant type of person in this system, therefore, is the *entrepreneur*.

Within the sustainable food movement (and more so on the part of participants of action groups than of practitioners) there seems to be an attitude that all for-profit business is bad and that sustainable food businesses should be either community-interest companies or workers' cooperatives. I think this attitude is rather unfair, not to mention unhelpful, when it is directed at the entrepreneur.

I think this attitude particularly unfair when you consider that small-business owners are often not only the hardest-working people in our community, but among the most poorly rewarded financially compared to the effort they put in. This is especially so when it comes to sustainable food, an industry that is notoriously difficult to make money in. I think the people who maintain this attitude also forget that the people they revere the most are themselves entrepreneurs; most *organic farmers* that I know of run for-profit businesses.

The sustainable food industry really wouldn't exist at all if it weren't for entrepreneurs. An organic farmer doesn't usually farm organically because they think they will make more money doing it that way, they do it because they passionately believe it is the right way to do things. In fact, because it is so much harder to make a profit while upholding strong ethical values, this activity almost exclusively becomes the preserve of the entrepreneur, because it takes that rather special type of character who is prepared to forego the comfort of a dependable salary, take on extraordinary levels of risk, and subject themselves to enormous workloads and stress in order to offer something to society that has authentic values.

It's crude to think that entrepreneurs are only motivated by money. Of course, all entrepreneurs want to see their businesses succeed, but the motivation behind that is much more complex than simply a desire to make money. There is a gulf of difference between a local food entrepreneur and a multi-national corporation. Local food entrepreneurism exists on a much more 'human' scale. If a small-business owner becomes successful after years of hard work then good luck to them; they deserve it because they have provided a service that is valued by society.

*Adrian Izzard of Wild Country Organics has won awards
for his exceptionally good produce.*

So much of the innovation, creativity and passion in the food industry comes from entrepreneurs. Two of the farmers who supply The Cambridge Organic Food Company are Adrian Izzard of Wild Country Organics and Tyler Cotton of Dynamic Organics. Both of them started their own organic farming businesses from scratch, and both hold themselves to exceptionally high standards. The food they each produce is out of this world. Food of such exceptional quality simply wouldn't be on the market were it not for the dedication of characters such as Adrian and Tyler. In 2012, Leo Riethoff and his wife Charley started a new business called Steak & Honour, selling high-end beef-burgers from the back of a classic Citroën H van. There is now an exciting and vibrant street food scene in Cambridge as several other entrepreneurs followed Leo's pioneering lead. Just outside Cambridge there is a shop called Organic Health which is run by Jackie Williams. Organic Health carries one of the most extensive ranges of organic and specialist diet foods I know of, and Jackie herself has an encyclopaedic knowledge of the products and their ingredients. Kyung Lim makes a product called Asado Sauce in small batches at home and sells it locally. It is inspired by her childhood experience living in Argentina, is made from natural ingredients, and is an absolute taste sensation. There are so many more local food practitioners I would have loved to include in this paragraph. It is people like Adrian, Tyler, Leo, Jackie and Kyung that make the food scene in Cambridge what it is. These guys are real food heroes, and they are, of course, all entrepreneurs.

No one is 'commanding' these business owners, they do what they do of their own free will. Creating the visionary, sustainable food system we all dream of doesn't have to be a leviathan uphill struggle, it can happen quite effortlessly simply by harnessing the latent entrepreneurial potential which already exists in the community. All that is required is the existence of favourable trading conditions for local businesses. With this in place all manner of food entrepreneurs will emerge to take advantage of the new opportunity, and from here you are well on the way towards having an inspirational Local Food Ecosystem.

Who controls the system?

'Control food and you control the people.'

Henry Kissinger

The issue of control in the food system is a really important one. I shouldn't need to explain how important food is to you as an individual or at the population level, and the tremendous position of power held by those who control the food system. Much of this power currently lies with an alarmingly small number of mega corporations who have control over the nutritional value of food, methods of food production and land use, and the price and distribution of food. What is especially concerning is what motivates these corporations; do you really think it is *your* health and well-being? Or the health and well-being of the planet? The head offices of these corporations are in remote places, often different countries, and you have a difficult task if you want your voice to be heard by them.

If we want to redress the balance of power in our food supply then creating resilient local food systems which exist outside the control of large corporations is a must. This, really, is the essence of food sovereignty. Be in no doubt about this: as a citizen, choosing to spend your money on locally grown food is one of the most emphatic political statements you can make.

Of course, if local food systems are to exist in juxtaposition to the corporate food industry in terms of power and control, then those food systems must be egalitarian in their own structure. Here we see another point of correlation between the Local Food Ecosystem and a natural ecosystem, because there is no hierarchy in nature. There is no master planner who controls how the system functions or how individuals should behave. Individuals in a natural ecosystem look after their own self-interests first and foremost, but in a way which is mindful of the fact that the ecosystem is their home and so their self-interests are best served by taking care of the environment.

Choosing to spend your money on locally grown food is one of the most emphatic political statements you can make.

In nature all components of the ecosystem are equally important. Any individual would not be able to exist outside the ecosystem, but likewise each component of the ecosystem performs a valuable role in its functioning. In the Local Food Ecosystem no member is considered more or less important than their fellow members, whether they are the poshest restaurant in town or a soup kitchen for the homeless run by a community group. The top-end restaurant acknowledges that the soup kitchen performs an important role in the same community that supports it. Each enterprise is mutually respectful of the other's role in the functioning of the Ecosystem, and in return the Ecosystem is able to deliver products and services that are right for each of their needs. It is through this characteristic that the Local Food Ecosystem can achieve **equitable distribution** of food throughout the community.

Natural ecosystems are reliant on the ability of individuals to self-organise. The Local Food Ecosystem also operates on this principle. If there is one thing I've learnt from the many years I've spent working and doing business with local traders (especially organic farmers), it is that they do like to do their own thing. People, especially the entrepreneurial type, value the freedom to be able to work to their own rhythm, implement their own ideas, and do the things which motivate them and that they enjoy. Any attempts to coerce or control such characters naturally meets with resistance.

The tendency in nature isn't to overcome resistance, but to 'go with the flow' instead. You get the best out of people when you allow them to gravitate towards the tasks that motivate them, and let them solve problems their own way. Conversely, 'command and control' forms of governance are energy intensive and inefficient. Empowerment of others achieves so much more for much less effort. The strength and potential of the Local Food Ecosystem concept lies in allowing and empowering practitioners within the food system to be individuals, to self-organise and to concentrate on doing the things that they want to do; if someone loves making jam, and are really good at it, then we want them to be spending as much of their time as possible making jam, and not so much time performing the less enjoyable (from their perspective) or productive tasks such as deliveries and paperwork (which the Food Hub can do on their behalf).

I'm aware of the slight contradiction in the concept here; I am advocating an egalitarian system in which members self-organise, and in which no single body has overall control, while at the same time talking in terms of 'supply chain coordination' or 'supply chain management'.

What are 'coordination' and 'management' if not a form of control? This quandary is addressed by the ownership model, but we will come on to that later.

The Local Food Ecosystem is a concept which anyone should be able to adopt as their own and figure out how the principles best apply to themselves and their area. A group of like-minded local food enterprises might reach out to one another and form the nucleus of their own Local Food Ecosystem, simply by making a pact to prioritise trading with one another whenever possible over buying food that originates from beyond the local area. The Ecosystem can, and will, grow from there. For these reasons I would describe uptake of the Local Food Ecosystem in terms of it being a *movement*. The Local Food Ecosystem is a blueprint for how new economic thinking can be applied to the food industry, along with a set of principles and values which individuals and food practitioners are invited to interpret in a way that suits their area.

I am not so egotistical as to claim that the 'Local Food Ecosystem' is the movement. Not at all. The movement I have in mind already exists and has already been going on for over a century as a counterculture to industrial food production. It is a movement which includes thousands of organic farmers in the UK, thousands more people who own or work for 'values-driven' food enterprises, the many citizens who belong to organisations such as the Soil Association, Landworkers' Alliance or Slow Food in the UK, not to mention the vast majority of the UK population who purchase at least some certified organic food on a regular basis. It is a movement which convenes regularly at events such as the Oxford Real Farming Conference and the Sustainable Food Places Conference. It is a movement which similarly includes dedicated practitioners and citizens in every other country of the world. I am, of course, talking about the *sustainable food* movement.

The Local Food Ecosystem is an idea which I merely hope will enable this remarkable, and hugely important, sustainable food movement to continue to grow. It creates a more favourable trading environment for locally and sustainably produced food, allowing existing sustainable food businesses to flourish and encouraging new ones to start. And because the Local Food Ecosystem concept considerably lessens waste and the environmental impact of food distribution, it is a model which is highly

More like this please. A vibrant local food economy would feature many independent food shops which are outlets for food distributed through the Local Food Ecosystem. Radmore Farm Shop in Cambridge sells locally grown organic fruit and vegetables and also 'zero waste' products, where customers bring their own packaging.

relevant in terms of addressing climate change; something which further bolsters the sustainable food movement's stake in the food system.

For as long as costs, such as environmental damage, continue to be externalised then independent small businesses face an extraordinary disadvantage in trying to compete with global corporations for market share. Their economies of scale, dominion of the marketplace, marketing and political clout and ownership of infrastructure assets are so overwhelming that any independent small business struggles simply to exist, let alone thrive. However, a *movement* of small businesses, passionately independent but united by common goals and values and working in Harmony with one another, *would* be able to command a sizeable share of the market.

Competition within the Local Food Ecosystem

As a small-business owner myself, few things instil a feeling of anxiety within me as much as finding out that a new competitor is starting up in the area. Seeing their advertisements, social media posts or vans out and about really gets under my skin. I think this is a very natural reaction that any other small-business owner will relate to; we all work so hard to survive in such a marginal market sector that a newcomer can be perceived as a real threat. However, this reaction it is not a productive one. For starters, competition is a fact of life that you have no control over and if you engage too much in worrying about it you just stress yourself out.

Secondly, a little healthy competition is actually a good thing, especially within the Local Food Ecosystem.

In the previous chapter I talked about 'survival of the fittest', and how, in nature, this is a mechanism for personal development of the species rather than one which grants one species dominion over all others. All the greatest sportsmen and women were driven to extraordinary levels of performance and achievement by the presence of another equally high-performing rival. In business the presence of a competitor is a challenge for you to improve your own performance in order to keep your own competitive advantage, but this often results in a positive outcome for both businesses. It is an effect we have witnessed in the brewing industry. In recent years there has been a renaissance in the craft beer and micro-brewing industry. Many cities can boast not one or two, but *several* artisanal brewing businesses. The competition these small breweries provide for each other means that there is a fantastic variety of very-high-quality beers on the market. This is great for consumers. But for the breweries themselves, rather than competing within a niche, a whole new market sector has been created which has taken market share away from the giant brewing corporations. More jobs in the brewing industry have been created, small brewing businesses are able to flourish, and consumers are presented with greater choice and quality. This is exactly the kind of vibrant local market economy we want for food, and which the Local Food Ecosystem promises to create.

The instinct of small business is to want to suppress its competition. But to create a vibrant Local Food Ecosystem newcomers to the system should be welcomed, even if their offering is similar to your own. If you rise to the challenge, and your competitor does as well, this won't result in one of you going out of business; it results in two really competent businesses who have just created a burgeoning market sector. Competition between peers is good. It is unfair competition and market dominance from corporate giants that we should be struggling against.

Conclusion

Hopefully in this chapter I have managed conjure up a vision of a local system in which there are plenty of farmers who choose to adopt sustainable production methods and market their produce locally, in which no matter where you live there is an independent food shop that sells local produce within easy reach (preferably walking distance), in which there is a proliferation of artisanal food-processing businesses who are adding value to locally produced ingredients, and in which you know you can go to work, send your kids to school, or go out for the evening safe in the knowledge that there is good, healthy food made from local ingredients to be found there.

Hopefully I have also conjured up a vision where these local enterprises, while remaining independent and competitive in their own right, also operate with a sense of unity with one another, taking collective responsibility for the provision of good food to their local community and the environmental impact of the system. And they do this by interacting with one another as much as possible and adopting circular processes for the management of resources.

It is eminently possible to achieve this vision. The only thing that really needs to happen is for trading conditions to be right. Provided there is a good opportunity for it to flourish you can rely upon entrepreneurial ingenuity to identify and fulfil local gaps in the market, come up with innovative new products, or even just lovingly perform time-honoured artisanal food activities really well. There are multitudes of people who would love to set up a micro-brewery, run a street food stall, or turn their hand to market gardening, and who would absolutely do so if they felt they would be adequately rewarded for doing it. Creating this fertile environment for food start-ups requires two things. It needs people to support their local food economy by choosing to buy food from local businesses. And it needs good infrastructure to create the interconnectivity that is vital for the functioning of the Local Food Ecosystem, and provide services which give local food businesses a competitive edge.

The Food Hub provides this infrastructure and these services. But the Local Food Ecosystem concept goes further than this. The 'services which give local food businesses a competitive edge' include some specific food supply chain coordination techniques which help achieve the objectives of eliminating waste, reducing environmental impact, and equitable distribution of food. These techniques are covered in the next chapter.

What the Local Food Ecosystem means to me: David Booth

David Booth is general manager at the Cambridge Organic Food Company, along with Rob Lasham. In this piece David tells us how reusable packaging is an inherent feature of the company's operations, and indeed how the attitude towards empty boxes is indicative of a culture of environmental awareness within the company.

We love our veg boxes! At Cambridge Organic, we are not only very proud of the veggies we put into our boxes, but we also have a deep affection for the cardboard boxes themselves. We try only to use the boxes which originally came to us bearing fruit or veg. If we can avoid it, we don't want to cause any more trees to be felled just to manufacture our packaging.

The sort of box we need is always in short supply. That's because the majority of our produce comes from local farms in large, re-useable trays which we can either take back to the farm when we make the next collection, or the farmer can take away if he or she delivers their produce directly to us. That's one of the great things about getting so much of our food directly from local producers: the possibility of returning and re-using the packaging. Once a supply chain is a chain, with multiple links, the chances of any packaging making its way back to the initial producer diminishes. As many of those links might well be 'one-way' – via pallet or container – there is no chance of the packaging getting back to the farm. It's exciting to think how the Food Hub will allow us to retain and re-use a greater range of packaging within the nexus of local food producers.

The boxes we use are ones which contain produce we've bought in to supplement what we get locally. We ask our members to return their empty veg box each week, so once a box goes into circulation, we hope it will be re-used many times over. But not every box comes back and boxes are lost to rain and collapse and the indelible dried remains of the odd squidgy orange. Over time, of course, they get scruffier and tattier, but they are so precious to us that we often patch them up with tape to get a few more uses out of them.

That's what seems remarkable about our attitude to the boxes: we treat something that would otherwise be waste as a valuable resource, a resource so valuable that we are prepared to mend them when they fall apart. I said we love our boxes, which might seem a bit extreme, but I think there is an emotional connection there. I remember times when, out delivering, I would see one of our boxes being used as permanent storage in someone's kitchen and the brief, hot feeling of indignation that rose in my chest. While writing this piece, a colleague, Crow, has popped into the office. He wanted me to get in touch with one of the members on his Friday route: he said they must leave their empty box outside exposed to the elements from one week to the next, so it's nearly always soggy and falls apart when he collects it. The fact that he cared enough to ask me to do that seemed very significant in the context of what I was thinking about. So, I have broken off from writing this to send a very hesitant and apologetic email asking – in what I hope is the nicest possible way – that they keep their boxes dry.

I think my own commitment to re-using our boxes has deepened over the years. I've worked for Cambridge Organic since 2006. Originally, I was doing the real work of packing and delivering our veg boxes; now my role has evolved to be just about managing. I remember the occasional doorstep where I would find veg boxes from other companies. The big veg-box companies, who distribute veg boxes over much of the country, have lovely boxes with their names and logos printed on. And the boxes fold up to be returned, which is pretty neat as well. I used to think, why can't we be a bit more professional and have some nifty branded boxes like those? But now I think that the real-world environmental benefits of trying to avoid the manufacture of virgin packaging far outweighs the marketing potential of having our logo slapped on the boxes. Although we miss out on the obvious opportunity of branded boxes, we can and should build a brand through clear communication that celebrates the re-use of our raggle-taggle collection of boxes.

We face a similar challenge with the Food Hub: the need to develop a brand and a narrative that not only clearly explains the environmental underpinning of a new way of doing things, but also makes it look pretty damn cool.

David Booth

A much-loved member of the team. David celebrates an important birthday (I won't say which one) by sharing his cake with the COFCO team.

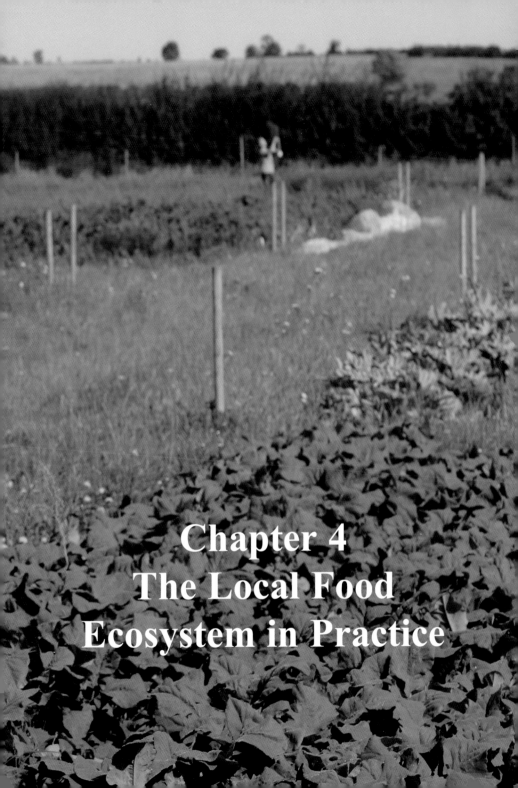

Chapter 4
The Local Food
Ecosystem in Practice

Chapter 4
The Local Food Ecosystem in Practice

Now that we have covered the philosophy of the Local Food Ecosystem concept, it is time to take a closer look at what this actually means in practice.

The main feature of the Local Food Ecosystem is that it considers the local food system as a whole. Rather than focussing on a narrow market segment and serving that segment with a linear supply chain, the Local Food Ecosystem serves a range of different types of food enterprise and balances their needs in a way in which everyone wins.

Once the Local Food Ecosystem has achieved a critical mass of members, and there is a good range of different types of food users in the system, then the stage is set to start implementing some rather remarkable new techniques in food supply chain coordination. Specifically there are two techniques that I will be describing in this chapter. The first of these is a method of ensuring that as much food as possible finds its way to a destination where it is valued, which, when functioning well, can completely eliminate systemic wastage of food. The other is a technique for optimising the distribution of food and minimising food miles and the associated emissions, which also enables resources to be **cycled** efficiently. Each of these techniques works to greater effect the more participation there is in the Local Food Ecosystem.

Eliminating systemic food waste

One of the main problems that the Local Food Ecosystem addresses is that of systemic food waste. Systemic food waste is food waste which is 'built in' to the food supply chain; an inevitable consequence of the modern food industry's 'need' to keep shelves filled and pantries well stocked. Let me give you an example.

One of the largest vegetable producers in the country once told us of a field of 100,000 lettuces which had to be written off. Apparently this was not an uncommon occurrence for them. They were perfectly good lettuces in every respect. In fact, the only reason those lettuces were wasted was because the supermarket chain that they were intended for had overestimated its requirements. Without a buyer it was uneconomical to harvest the lettuces, and they were simply ploughed back into the ground. The grower is not at all to blame for this; living as we do in an age of 24/7 convenience and the expectation that supermarket shelves will always be full, the penalties for the grower of under-supply are far greater than that of over-supply. Growers have no choice but grow enough produce to satisfy the greatest possible demand, and simply take the hit if the demand is less than anticipated. This is what I mean by systemic food waste.

If you analyse the case of the wasted lettuces and get to the root of why that particular instance of food waste occurred, the answer is that those lettuces were only ever intended for one end user. It was an end user who had very *rigid requirements*, not just in terms of quality or aesthetics, but also volume. Anything which fell outside those requirements was inevitably destined to be wasted. This is an inherent problem with linear supply chains.

In an optimally functioning Local Food Ecosystem everything that enters the system will find a destination where it is valued and nothing goes to waste.

This is a great example of how the Local Food Ecosystem is a better way to manage supply chains. Unlike linear supply chains, which focus solely on the needs of one type of end user, the Local Food Ecosystem balances the needs of different types of food user, some who have rigid requirements, and some who can be more *flexible* with regard to their inputs. This way, any food that is not needed by the first user is much more likely to find an alternative destination. In fact, in an optimally functioning Local Food Ecosystem, where inputs are being balanced with outputs and a good range of food users are being served, the food that isn't needed by the first user *automatically* finds an alternative home. In an optimally functioning Local Food Ecosystem everything that enters the system will find a destination where it is valued and nothing goes to waste.

The technique for achieving zero waste begins with the principle of **balance**. This is a very basic principle of any waste reduction strategy: quite simply, if inputs exactly balance with outputs then you have created a system of optimum efficiency which has zero waste. In the Local Food Ecosystem the volume of produce coming out of the system is balanced with the volume of produce coming into it.

That is easier said than done, of course. The food system is 'chaotic', with many variables that can affect supply and demand (harvest failure, consumer trends/choice, market prices etc.), so it is little wonder that the rigid, linear supply chains find it almost impossible to operate at optimum efficiency.

The magic of the Local Food Ecosystem is what happens to the produce as it travels through the system. A good Local Food Ecosystem will consist of a range of food users, including enterprises who have rigid requirements *and* enterprises who can be more flexible with regard to their inputs. The *total volume* of food required by the Local Food Ecosystem is calculated, and this is balanced with the total volume of food coming into the system. This way, there is the right amount of food to meet the needs of all the users. The most demanding food users (those with very rigid requirements) get the first pick of the produce that is available, but they pay a premium for the privilege. The enterprises who can be more flexible with regard to their inputs receive the food that was not needed by the rigid users. The defining principle of the flexible food user is that they want to receive a *quantity* of food, without necessarily being too fussed about which types of food they get, but they do get better value for money instead. We have called this technique 'Optimised Food–User Matching'. Nobody in the Local Food Ecosystem is receiving 'cast-offs' or 'surplus'; the food all comes from the same original source. The needs of all the food users are met, and the differentiation comes from the level of service that is received rather than the quality of the food. This way, *all* produce entering the system finds a destination where it is valued, and nothing goes to waste.

This technique is perhaps better explained by considering the real-life business operation which has inspired it …

The Cambridge Organic Food Company is an organic box scheme enterprise which packs and delivers fruit and vegetable boxes containing produce sourced from farms local to Cambridge. It is also a zero-food-waste enterprise; around ten tonnes of fresh produce are handled each week and *none* of it is ever thrown in the bin.

COFCO, or more specifically Rob, has become adept at predicting the number of vegetable boxes which are to be packed and delivered over the course of a week. Knowing the total volume of produce which is to come out of the system means it is possible to balance this with the total volume of produce which needs to come into the system, and order those inputs with a reasonable degree of accuracy. So if, for example, 1,000 boxes are to be delivered, and each box contains an average of twenty units of produce, then Rob will know that 20,000 units of produce are needed to fill those boxes and he will order accordingly. COFCO principally offers two different ranges of veg boxes, which are differentiated by the degree to which customers can influence their box contents. The 'Choice' range is a completely bespoke service which allows customers to choose their entire box contents, but they pay more for this privilege. 'Original' boxes do not allow customers to influence the contents of the box, but they get better value for money. At the start of the packing process the correct amount of produce to fulfil the day's boxes is set out. The Choice boxes are packed first, ensuring that the Choice customers get what they requested. The Original boxes are packed with the produce remaining after the Choice boxes have been filled. The produce in the Original boxes is in no way inferior to that in the Choice boxes; it all comes from the same pot of fresh, locally grown organic veg. The differentiation is all based on the level of service the different types of customers receive. Everyone gets what they want. Customers to whom choice and service are more important than price are happy, as are those to whom value for money is more important than choice. Through this process, all of the produce entering the system finds a destination where it is valued.

Let's take a moment to further consider the characteristics of the Optimised Food–User Matching system and the benefits it brings.

Aside from the fact that this is a zero-waste system, it also has the benefit of being able to adapt according to what is available. COFCO's profile of suppliers includes some small-scale local producers, some large-scale local producers and some wholesale suppliers. This system enables us to accept pretty much everything that the small-scale producers want to supply us with, even if the quantity of any particular line is far fewer than the number of boxes being delivered. It also adapts very well to seasonality, being able to utilise seasonal gluts, for example.

The other significant point I'd like to make about the COFCO system is that it enables the total cost of food to be varied for different customer types, but the price differential is based on levels of service, NOT on levels of quality. It is this characteristic that points to a way in which food might be distributed more equitably and made more accessible to people with a smaller budget for food.

The Local Food Ecosystem technique works along similar principles, but applies them to business distribution rather than retail sales. In order to extrapolate from the COFCO system and make it work for wholesale supply, the first task is to identify which members of the Local Food Ecosystem are the equivalents of the Choice and Original veg box customers.

The Choice customers are the easiest to identify, as this is the way that most food businesses operate. Shops, restaurants, catering establishments and most other commercial food buyers are accustomed to ordering whatever types of produce they require in the expectation that it will all arrive, in prime condition, at their specified time.

So who are the equivalent of the Original veg box customers? Which food-using enterprises can be flexible with regards to their inputs in return for a lower total cost of food? The first answer is food-processing businesses who will add value to ingredients (by making soups, sauces, pickles, preserves etc.), and the other is organisations who make healthy, fresh produce more accessible within low-income communities.

The total cost of food is varied at different levels of the Local Food Ecosystem according to the needs of the different types of food users and the degree of flexibility they can tolerate within their operation. This is explained in further detail in the '**Membership-based revenue model**' section in Chapter 5.

Because the Local Food Ecosystem is based upon direct trade between local food enterprises, there is also an element of free-market economics which will further affect the total cost of food, potentially exacerbating the price differential at the extremes of the user spectrum. And this can bring further benefit to members of the Local Food Ecosystem. Sellers will be encouraged to apply 'dynamic pricing' to ensure that all their produce is sold; starting out at a high price to try and achieve the best price from the high-demanding buyers, but then reducing price when demand wanes to ensure that everything else gets sold. This benefits the producer as they realise the best possible financial return and sell everything that they have. It achieves the objective of eliminating waste. And this further reduces the cost of food available to the flexible-user groups.

This type of supply chain coordination also makes provision for sub-prime-quality produce (i.e. 'wonky veg') to find a route to market. There is no reason why wonky veg cannot also be traded within the Local Food Ecosystem, and indeed growers will be encouraged to do so in the interests of minimising waste and maximising their returns. Because the Local Food Ecosystem includes a wide range of food users, there is a likelihood that some of its members will find a use for it. And because the wonky veg will be collected from the farm at the same time as the other produce that is being distributed through the Local Food Ecosystem, it becomes more economically viable for this relatively low-value produce to be transported from the farm to its destination. The producer might realise a modest income from this produce, whereas it might otherwise have been donated for free, or just wasted. And it shouldn't be assumed that the wonky veg will automatically go to the 'flexible' food users. The trading platform is a free market and there is no reason why a more demanding food user couldn't buy the wonky veg, thereby helping to redefine attitudes towards less-than-perfect foods which still have terrific nutritional value.

A final point I'd like to make on the Optimised Food–User Matching technique and its ability to eliminate waste is that waste is only eliminated *within* the system, on a scale which is proportionate to the size of the Ecosystem. The Local Food Ecosystem is not a solution to industrial-scale wastage of food. For example, a Local Food Ecosystem operating in a city of 125,000 people (such as Cambridge) is never going to be able to find homes for the 100,000 lettuces described previously. It may be that elements of the Optimised Food–User Matching technique can be applied to large-scale food industry, and anything which mitigates this type of waste would be great, of course, but on the whole resources such as food can be used much more efficiently and without waste when it is managed at a local scale.

Flexible food users

As you will have gathered in the last section, there is a very important role in the functioning of the Local Food Ecosystem that is performed by flexible food users. That is to say, food users and consumers who want some food but are quite open-minded and flexible when it comes to exactly what it is they are going to eat. It is saying, 'I'm going to eat what's available', rather than 'I'm going to eat what I want'. This attitude to food, while quite unorthodox in the commercial world, is actually the way most people throughout history have lived, and the way that many people in developing countries get by today. It is also a mindset that is much more relevant in mankind's efforts to tackle climate change: adapting our diets to crops that thrive in our local climate and eating with the seasons are good things to do if you are conscientious about the environment.

It is all well and good for individuals to make these sorts of dietary choices, and many people do, but it is much rarer to find an enterprise that operates with this attitude. What can we do to change this?

Adapting our diets to crops that thrive in our local climate and eating with the seasons are good things to do if you are conscientious about the environment.

One of the things people often say to me when I tell them about the wasted lettuces is 'couldn't the farmer have given them to charity, to feed people who are hungry?'. If only it were that simple. There are a number of reasons why this does not happen. The first is an economic reason: the farm is not going to receive any money for that produce, and yet there is a great deal of expense to be incurred harvesting and transporting it. Financially the grower is better off cutting their losses and leaving the produce in the field (a modest gain even; at least the lettuces will add a little nutrient to the soil when re-incorporated into it). Allowing unattended 'gleaners' in to harvest some of the produce brings all sorts of health & safety risks which farms are understandably reluctant to accept liability for. However, the most significant reason why it is so difficult to find a home for this unwanted produce is because the types of enterprises which could use it are so few and far between, and with good reason. They don't exist because linear supply chains, which hope that these enterprises will just magically sweep in and take anything which isn't needed, do not make provision for them. Despite their adaptability when it comes to which ingredients they will use, a flexible food-using enterprise still needs a reliable supply of those ingredients on a regular basis; you simply can't have a team of people on standby waiting for a glut of lettuces to appear, and systemic food waste is sporadic. A more sophisticated solution is required.

The difference in the Local Food Ecosystem is that there is always a proportion of the total volume of food being handled which is specifically intended for the flexible-user enterprises. In the same way that Original box customers are catered for in the COFCO system, provision is always made for the flexible food-using enterprises when balancing inputs and outputs. This way they always have a reliable and steady supply of produce, and consequently are able to create a viable business from this activity.

One point that I want to be really clear on, just in case you are assuming otherwise, is that the food used by the flexible food users is by no means waste or surplus food that was not used elsewhere. It isn't unsold veg that has sat on a shop shelf for a week or outgraded produce from the farm. No. The food used by flexible food-using enterprises is good-quality produce which has come straight from the farm. It is simply the produce which wasn't bought by the more demanding food users, and because enough food was brought into the system to satisfy the needs of both the demanding and the flexible users there is always a reliable supply of produce for everyone.

There are two types of food-using enterprises which can naturally adopt the role of the flexible food user in the Local Food Ecosystem, the first of which is organisations which make healthy, fresh food more accessible to low-income communities. There is an obvious and natural fit between consumer groups who are on a tight budget and a supply chain coordination system which needs to have within its profile of food users some buyers who pay less for food. In fact, this particular category of Local Food Ecosystem member pays nothing for their membership of the system, meaning the price paid for food is literally the same as the farmer's ex-farm price (theoretically the lowest possible price). This is how the Local Food Ecosystem achieves equitable distribution of food throughout the community.

The other category of flexible food users is food-processing businesses and catering businesses who will add value to whatever foods might be available without being prescriptive about what their ingredients are. Some progressive chefs already take this attitude, making a point of only preparing ingredients which are 'in season'. Soup making, fruit/vegetable preserving and conference catering are all examples of enterprises which could be carried out with a flexible attitude regarding the ingredients that are used. And because the flexible food users have access to food at a lower total cost than the more demanding members of the Local Food Ecosystem, there is ample opportunity for entrepreneurial ingenuity to fulfil this important role in the functioning of the Ecosystem.

A feature of the Food Hub building is the provision of incubator kitchen units, available to small food businesses and start-ups on flexible and affordable terms. One intention for these kitchens at the Food Hub is to stimulate the creation of new food enterprises who are flexible food users.

Supply chain coordination: cutting down on those food miles

The other innovative technique of the Local Food Ecosystem concept concerns the way food is physically moved from one place to another. It draws heavily on the principle of interconnectivity and the efficiency with which it is possible to deliver food to the places it is needed within a well-connected Local Food Ecosystem.

A significant use of energy and source of emissions in the food industry is associated with the transportation of food. Although food miles may not be the most significant source of emissions from the food industry, it certainly doesn't make sense to import produce into an area from a great distance away when produce of a similar type is being grown locally and exported out of the area. A little bit of common sense and joined-up thinking that ensured that the potatoes being grown in a field three miles away from a particular city ended up being the potatoes that were eaten in that city surely represents an 'easy win' in the quest to hit the carbon-reduction targets that our government has set.

Crisp packet recycling scheme. Savoursmiths make crisps using potatoes grown on their own farm just outside Cambridge. They are also pioneers in using crisp packets made from code 5 polypropylene, which are much easier to recycle than conventional crisp packets. Cambridge Food Hub has been supplying the crisps to pubs and cafés, including Bridges in Cambridge (pictured), along with a box in which customers can place their empty packets for recycling.

Food miles equals emissions. The Local Food Ecosystem promises to minimise the environmental impact of food distribution. A big part of this is a straightforward reduction of food miles, which the Local Food Ecosystem easily achieves at the macro level, but, as I am about to explain when describing this particular technique, it also manages it at the micro level. The environmental benefits associated with reduced food miles goes further than the savings in vehicle emissions. When food is dispatched over short distances you can get away without needing refrigerated transport; refrigerated lorries and vans are much less efficient as they are heavier, have a reduced load capacity, and need energy to run the chillers. Transporting food locally also means it can be done within the limited range of electric vehicles.

Food miles at the 'macro' scale accounts for any food which hasn't travelled directly from its point of production to its nearest main area of consumption; in other words the vast majority of all food, and certainly all food which has passed through a conventional supply chain. Lengthy supply chains also mean lots of 'additional' food miles, with food often travelling from its point of production to a succession of traders, packhouses and distribution centres before arriving at its end user. It is not unheard of for produce to travel hundreds of miles, only to end up just a few miles away from the place where it was originally produced (at which point it will probably be labelled as 'locally grown'). Each summer the University of Cambridge buys a significant quantity of strawberries. The strawberries are grown in a village just outside Cambridge. However, they come to Cambridge via New Covent Garden market in London. Those strawberries travel over a hundred miles, only to be consumed around five miles away from the place they were grown.

Food distributed within the Local Food Ecosystem is locally produced and therefore has significantly fewer food miles than any food which has travelled through a conventional, linear supply chain.

As food systems have become increasingly industrialised, the infrastructure for supporting local trade of food has eroded. The reason why the aforementioned strawberries need to travel to London and back before being used by the University is because the infrastructure for getting them there directly simply doesn't exist. In fact, the whole landscape of the UK has changed, grouping certain land use types in different geographical areas depending on the type of infrastructure that exists in that area for handling certain foods (for example, a lot of sugar beet is grown in west Suffolk due to the proximity of the Silver Spoon factory, whereas there isn't so much dairy-cattle farming as the area is poorly serviced by infrastructure for milk). This does bring certain efficiency advantages for the respective industries, but it also results in a degree of specialisation into certain types of agriculture which lessens the ability of an area to be self-sufficient and feed its population with a range of locally produced foods.

Food hubs, which are at the heart of the Local Food Ecosystem concept, provide the infrastructure necessary for food which has been grown locally to make its way directly into local markets. And the very existence of such infrastructure will hopefully encourage some food producers to adapt their business models and start producing food specially for the local markets.

So the food miles saving brought about by the Local Food Ecosystem at the macro level is clear and obvious; however, the concept goes further, and also helps to reduce food miles at the *micro* level.

Micro-scale food miles is the transportation of food from local producers and businesses directly into their local market. While this would appear to be the route to market that incurred the fewest possible food miles, the Local Food Ecosystem can make this process even more efficient.

Local food networks are often characterised by a number of small-scale food businesses who will deliver relatively small quantities of their products to local independent outlets. Often journeys will be made by several small businesses who are essentially visiting the same outlets. The Local Food Ecosystem concept means that products from a number of local businesses are delivered to these outlets in one van. This brings convenience for the buyer, who doesn't have to deal with several deliveries and invoices. And it is advantageous for the sellers as the distribution costs incurred when delivering a relatively small order can make the business unviable.

And there is a third way in which the Local Food Ecosystem helps to minimise food miles even further, through better coordination of the supply chain. This is by actively seeking opportunities to not just deliver goods or collect goods, but to do both things at the same time. In other words, when a Food Hub vehicle is at an establishment making a delivery, it is very simple and cost-effective to collect something and take it away. It could be that a food-processing businesses takes delivery of some raw ingredients, but sends some finished products back to the Food Hub for distribution throughout the Local Food Ecosystem. Perhaps a retailer taking receipt of some goods might have other stock that it has sold to other members of the Local Food Ecosystem and needs to be delivered. Goods and resources are effectively catching a 'piggy-back ride', either to the distribution centre or directly to their final destination. Vehicles are never empty, so 'empty' miles are being eliminated. It is through this technique that the Local Food Ecosystem can also enable the **cycling** of resources, and further address the issue of food waste.

Another way in which food is wasted on a regular basis is through surplus from the retail and catering industries. Surplus is an inevitable characteristic of the retail trade: shoppers have to be tempted into the shop by an abundant supply of fresh produce, and the confidence of knowing that the items they need will be available from the retailer. It is therefore necessary for the retailer to always stock more than will be sold. Any retailer who attempted to minimise their waste by allowing their shelves to run low would risk losing custom to a less conscientious retailer who continued to provide customers with 'what they want'. So once again, this type of food waste is inherent to the current way of doing things. Likewise, food-service businesses often have to buy and prepare more food than will be sold: sandwich makers and fast-food restaurants need to have meals ready for people to 'grab and go'; catering companies prepare buffets with far more food than people want to eat; a restaurant doesn't want to disappoint its customers by telling them that their desired menu item has run out. Although there have been very welcome advances when it comes to mitigating this type of waste, it is unlikely that this type of surplus will ever be eradicated completely. Whenever this type of food waste occurs there will always be somebody somewhere who would welcome receipt of that food. The trouble is, at this stage of the food's life cycle it has become significantly less valuable financially, and the cost of getting the food from its present location to the willing recipient doesn't make any economic sense whatsoever.

Surplus food is an excellent example of a resource which could be collected at the same time as a food delivery is being made. That surplus food then 'piggy-backs' a lift on a journey that was being made anyway, and can find its way to a new home far more cost-effectively than if a special journey was made just to pick it up. Although still in a developmental stage, the Food Hub in Cambridge already offers this service. When dispatching produce to wholesale buyers, a delivery route is chosen with a community fridge as the final destination. As the van goes round delivering to retail outlets it will collect any unsold produce those shops wish to donate, which is then dropped off at the community fridge at the end of the round. It hardly takes any extra effort at all.

Another resource which can be cycled thanks to this technique of supply chain coordination is reusable packaging. Recycling packaging is generally considered to be a good thing, but *reusing* packaging is even better. The implementation of reusable food packaging is enormously problematic within a lengthy linear supply chain; I just can't envision a way for things like jam jars and bottles to make their way back along the supply chain to the processor who could refill them. However, it is ever so simple to do at a local level and with a short supply chain. In fact, we have been doing it for years at The Cambridge Organic Food Company;

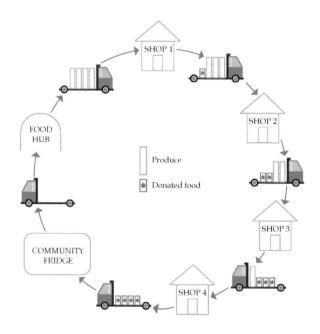

This diagram shows how incorporating surplus food redistribution into the same process as commercial food deliveries results in a much more efficient way for this activity to happen.

the members of the box scheme return the empty boxes to us each week when the next box is delivered. More recently, we have started collecting empty returnable jars on behalf of Totally Cultured, a local sauerkraut producer who is a member of the Local Food Ecosystem. It is early days, but the potential of this concept is blatantly obvious.

Recycling is good, reusing is even better. The shorter the supply chain, the easier it is for reusable packaging to efficiently make its way back to the producer to be used again. Totally Cultured will take back the jars they pack their sauerkraut and kimchi into, cleanse them, and refill them. In a functioning Local Food Ecosystem reusable packaging schemes can become commonplace.

An example of this technique of supply chain coordination has already been implemented to great effect in another of Cambridge Food Hub's activities: the 'Green Coffee Shop Scheme'. In the Green Coffee Shop Scheme, products (most notably an organic 'barista' style oat milk) are being delivered to coffee shops in and around Cambridge. However, at the same time as making the delivery, the van driver also collects the coffee shop's used coffee grounds. These grounds are then taken to a recycling plant which turns them into 'coffee logs' (a combustible solid fuel which can be burned instead of wood). The coffee grounds have no monetary value, so it simply isn't economically viable to make a specific journey to collect the grounds and take them to the recycling centre. After the coffee grounds have been delivered, the van then loads up again with coffee logs which come back to the Food Hub and are one of the products which are distributed. The van is never empty, and by triangulating the route it achieves a considerable saving in emissions compared to the journeys being made independently of each other:

Journey 1: van takes oat milk to coffee shops and collects used coffee grounds

Journey 2: van takes coffee grounds to recycling facility and collects coffee logs

Journey 3: van takes coffee logs to Food Hub

Compare this with the number of journeys that might be made without this particular form of supply chain coordination:

Journey 1: van delivers oat milk to coffee shops
Journey 2: empty van returns to base
Journey 3: empty refuse truck travels to coffee shop to collect coffee grounds
Journey 4: refuse truck delivers coffee grounds to recycling centre
Journey 5: empty refuse truck returns to base
Journey 6: empty van travels to recycling centre to collect coffee logs
Journey 7: van takes coffee logs to Food Hub

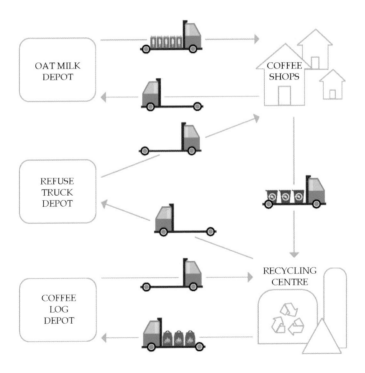

By employing this technique of supply chain coordination the 'empty van' miles are eliminated and the total number of journeys made can be more than halved.

In fact, the Green Coffee Shop Scheme proved to be so successful that after a short while the haul of used coffee grounds was great enough to be divided between two users: half goes to the recycling plant, and the other half goes to a local organic farm (Waterland Organics) where they are both composted and used as a medium for growing oyster mushrooms. And when the van is at the farm delivering the grounds, it also loads up with organic veg to be brought back to the Food Hub. Now that compost and organic veg have been brought in to the mix as well, we can begin to glimpse the enormous potential of the Local Food Ecosystem concept; just imagine the impact the system will have when this concept extends beyond coffee grounds, oat milk, coffee logs and veg to all the other food products and cyclable resources which could be exchanged within the nexus that is the Local Food Ecosystem.

Conclusion

The more members of the Local Food Ecosystem there are, the more interconnections there will be. The more connections there are, the greater the ability to implement the supply chain coordination techniques described in this chapter. With just a little bit of joined-up thinking it is possible to balance the needs of different types of food users and simultaneously achieve the three desirable outcomes of eliminating systemic waste, distributing food more equitably throughout the community, and significantly reducing the emissions associated with food distribution. Proof of concept for these supply chain coordination techniques has already been achieved. For all this to happen the right infrastructure needs to be in place. This infrastructure is provided by the Food Hub.

What the Local Food Ecosystem means to me: Paul Robinson

Paul Robinson is an organic farmer located close to Cambridge. His farm, Waterland Organics, hosts a terrific community-supported agriculture scheme called 'Cambridge Cropshare', and also participates in the 'Green Coffee Shop Scheme' as a destination for some of the used coffee grounds, which are composted and used as medium for growing oyster mushrooms.

At Waterland Organics we grow a large variety of different fruit and vegetables. There are a couple of reasons we do this. For a start, it makes our farm more biologically diverse, which in turn makes our organic farm more ecologically stable and less susceptible to pests and diseases. It also means we can offer local outlets like Arjuna Wholefoods and COFCO a wide range of the freshest local produce as well as keeping our CSA members stocked with the freshest vegetables.

However, there is a reason the large organic businesses do not do this: it is time-inefficient and the least likely way of providing good financial returns. It is certainly not a business model Henry Ford would have approved of. This is where the Food Hub is a great help. It saves us time delivering as it picks up and delivers the produce to COFCO. This time can be put to good use, doing what we should be doing: growing local organic vegetables with the least possible impact on the environment.

Not only do we get vegetables picked up but we get spent coffee grounds, picked up from Cambridge Coffee outlets, delivered to us at the same time. The amount of this coffee waste is often around the five hundred kilogram mark. The amount of produce we load in the van for the return journey is often around the same weight. The synchronicity of this does not escape me. Every time vegetables leave our farm, they take some of the farm's fertility with them and this has to be replenished. This is not a new problem. In the nineteenth century, the German chemist Justus von Liebig wrote a letter to Gladstone pointing out the drop in productivity that would result from agricultural land if nutrients were not replenished. We can replace some of this fertility with green manures grown on the farm but the addition of nutrients from elsewhere is a godsend.

By combining the spent coffee grounds with our own wood chips we can make compost and this compost replenishes the fertility that has been loaded onto the van.

It is obvious that such a connected web of businesses working together in such a collaborative and sustainable way is not only good for the respective businesses but good for the environment as well.

Paul Robinson

Circularity in the supply chain. Coffee grounds collected as part of the 'Green Coffee Shop Scheme' are unloaded at Waterland Organics. They will be used for compost and for growing oyster mushrooms. After the coffee grounds are unloaded the van is filled with organic veg, which goes back to the Food Hub.

On Paul's farm it is hard to tell where nature ends and farming begins. Paul himself is completely in tune with the ecology of his farm, and he has developed an astonishing amount of wisdom and understanding through working closely with nature for many years. Waterland Organics is unquestionably an enterprise that works in Harmony with nature.

Chapter 5
Putting the Theory into Practice: the Business Model for the Food Hub

Chapter 5
Putting the Theory into Practice: the Business Model for the Food Hub

If at this stage the Local Food Ecosystem sounds exciting and progressive, and something that you would like to see in your own area, then the question you may be asking now is 'How?' How can you go about creating a Local Food Ecosystem in your own area?

The strategy for creating a Local Food Ecosystem is to first create favourable conditions for local trade to take place. If, all of a sudden, the trading environment were to change so that it became viable and prosperous to run a small food enterprise, then you could expect to see an explosion in the number of new food start-up businesses, of farms which diversify in order to address the local market and of established independent food enterprises which really begin to flourish. It would be the tipping point from which a burgeoning and vibrant local food economy would emerge.

There are three factors that lead to favourable trading conditions: good levels of consumer demand, reduced costs (achieved the right way, which I will come to later) and provision of the necessary infrastructure. Consumer demand is something which is beyond our control (although demand for good food has been rising steadily and hopefully will continue to do so), but reducing costs and providing infrastructure are two things we *can* do something about. Provision of the infrastructure is basically what the Food Hub is and does, and the cost reduction results from the techniques of supply chain management it implements.

By this stage of the book the distinction between the 'Local Food Ecosystem' and the 'Food Hub' should hopefully be clear. The Local Food Ecosystem is a concept for a local food system in which local, independent food businesses are abundant and thriving, in which locally and sustainably produced food takes centre stage, and in which the supply chain of food is coordinated to meet social and environmental objectives.

The Food Hub on the other hand is a much more clearly defined business operation, the purpose of which is to stimulate and support the functioning of the Local Food Ecosystem, which it does through the provision of services and facilities that will be described in this chapter. In particular, the Food Hub provides the infrastructure which enables local businesses to trade directly with one another.

In this chapter I am going to describe the business model for the Food Hub that we are in the process of establishing in *Cambridge*. I think it's important to understand that this is the case, because while I am pretty well tuned in to the food needs of Cambridge, the needs of a larger city such as London, or a rural region such as mid-Wales, are going to be very different. With this in mind, I would say that the business model described in this chapter is *a* way of creating a Local Food Ecosystem in an area, but it is not necessarily *the* way of creating a Local Food Ecosystem. Food hubs, like Local Food Ecosystems, should be unique and perfectly suited to the needs of their own geographical area and community.

What the Food Hub does

the Food hub brings you food
in a nice way and itf fresh
Food From the ground.

Melody Catchpole, age 7.

The Food Hub exists to enable the functioning of the Local Food Ecosystem.

Although the Local Food Ecosystem is an egalitarian system, free from 'control', which functions according to principles of self-organisation, this system is not going to come into being spontaneously; it does need some work and effort to get the ball rolling. Also, for a Local Food Ecosystem to achieve some of the 'higher-level' functions, such as 'circular' delivery routes and Optimised Food–User Matching, then these processes do need to be coordinated by someone. This is the role of the

Food Hub. The first step in creating a Local Food Ecosystem is to ask the questions 'why is the local food network not behaving like a Local Food Ecosystem at the moment?' and 'what services and facilities would be needed to enable a Local Food Ecosystem to function?' The answer to these questions should help identify the services and facilities that the Food Hub needs to provide.

At the consultation meeting which took place in Cambridge in 2013[5] several local problems and needs were identified. One of these was that Cambridge is a hard place in which to establish a new food business. Rent and rates on commercial buildings in and around the city are very high and this is a significant barrier for many would-be food entrepreneurs starting up. In fact, many of the small-scale/artisanal food businesses in Cambridge at present literally operate from the proprietors' domestic kitchens, with little prospect of being able to scale up into a commercial operation. Many local catering businesses are priced out of the expensive city centre restaurant or café properties, leaving them to be occupied instead by chain restaurants (although this isn't entirely bad as, thanks to the inventiveness of entrepreneurs, Cambridge now has a vibrant street food scene and a market square that is well worth visiting when you are feeling hungry). On top of all this there is the sheer difficulty of trying to establish a new business in a sector which is so utterly dominated by global giants, who command massive economies of scale and control over the majority of routes to market. How could a person possibly hope to set up a cake-making business when a fully finished cake can be bought from a supermarket for less than the cost of their ingredients?

Another significant problem identified is a lack of distribution infrastructure for linking local producers directly with the marketplace. We have already discussed the locally grown strawberries that have to go on a 100-mile round trip, but that is just the tip of the iceberg. Cambridge is surrounded by very productive land, particularly to the north where there are the fens, so it is an absolute shame that more of the food being produced there does not make its way directly into the city.

This lack of local distribution infrastructure is yet another barrier for small food-processing businesses. Imagine a budding food entrepreneur who wanted to start a business adding value to locally grown produce,

---

5. Refer to 'The evolution of the idea' in Chapter 1.

let's say a range of artisanal cordials made from locally grown fruit. This is a retail product that is mainly to be sold in shops. Well, most food retail happens in supermarkets, and this route to market is not at all easy for our prospective start-up. Instead they are left with a handful of independent specialist food shops and farm shops. Now, these establishments are perfectly fine places for the cordial to be sold; you might even say there is a perfect 'fit' between the product and the establishment. However, the volume of sales of specialist products in such outlets is likely to be modest. Without local distribution infrastructure in place our cordial maker has no option but to deliver the goods themselves. Let's say they are based in a village and have to deliver a case of twelve bottles to a deli in the city centre; it is eight miles in each direction and an hour-long round trip by the time you have factored in having a quick chat with the shopkeeper and sorting out the paperwork. Even a small-engined family car has average running costs of about 40p per mile, so making that delivery adds about 53p to each bottle of cordial in vehicle running costs alone, and a whopping £1.30 if our entrepreneur were to factor in a Living Wage rate of pay for themselves (which they almost certainly do not). It just does not make economic sense at all, and this is why businesses such as this are few and far between.

I for one would love to live somewhere in which I could walk to a shop which sold locally made cordials, as well as fresh veg that had come straight from the fens and strawberries that haven't travelled for hundreds of miles unnecessarily. So, what needs to happen in order for this to be possible?

The answer, at least in Cambridge, although I expect the same is true in many other areas, is to lay on some pretty nifty local food distribution infrastructure which enables direct trade between local businesses. Just imagine for a moment what could happen if small food producers could be completely spared the cost of bringing their goods to market? How might the fortunes of our cordial magnate be changed if they could sell the case of cordial to the deli and incur zero costs getting it there while still receiving the same price for the goods? Well, this could be the difference between having a viable business and not. If it suddenly were to become viable to run a small artisanal food business then the floodgates would open and we could see an explosion in the number of cordial makers, market gardeners, jam makers, vegetable picklers, mushroom growers, kombucha brewers, fruit leather producers and every other wonderful and innovative food enterprise you could think of. The effect that provision of this infrastructure would have on the local food economy could be quite profound.

This, essentially, is what the Food Hub does: it provides the local food distribution infrastructure necessary for direct local trade to happen.

There are four elements to the service provided by the Food Hub: a trading platform, distribution infrastructure, supply chain coordination and the Food Hub building itself.

Direct trade on the trading platform

Throughout this book I have used the terms 'short supply chain' and 'direct trade'. The term 'short supply chain' refers to a supply chain in which the number of intermediaries handling the goods between the producer and the end user is small. Incidentally, the term has nothing to do with the *distance* the food has travelled; a specialist coffee roaster who buys coffee beans from a cooperative of farmers in Kenya and imports it themselves would still be

Tyler Cotton of Dynamic Organics adds the finishing touch to his legendary salad mix.

an example of a short supply chain even though the product was grown on another continent. All the same, short supply chains and direct trade are normally associated with local trade. When there are literally no intermediaries between the producer and the buyer this is known as direct trade; buying a box of eggs from a farmer at a farmers' market is an example of direct trade.

A typical, basic, food supply chain for fresh produce would be 'producer' sells to 'distributor' sells to 'wholesaler' sells to 'retailer' sells to 'end user'. When foods are processed the chain can become much longer; take a moment to think about the journey a grain of sugar might have to make between being part of a sugar cane grown in Mexico to being a chocolate bar sold in your local convenience shop.

The benefits of direct trade are that prices can be very fair; all of the added costs of the supply chain, such as transportation and traders' commissions, have been eliminated, meaning the removal of downward pressure on price for the producer (which is essential if the grower is to employ sustainable production techniques) and the buyer also pays much less than they would through a wholesaler. Buying directly also means the food is often fresher, and it maintains the knowledge link about who has grown the food and their standards of production. The downside of direct trade is that it is very inefficient to have to visit a number of different producers to obtain the range of foods that are required (part of the reason why fishmongers, greengrocers, bakers and butchers are disappearing from our high streets in favour of a supermarket in which all foods can be bought from the same establishment). Also, farmers do not want to be dealing with customers all the time, they are far too busy farming.

The benefits of buying from a wholesaler are that a range of goods can be purchased from the same source. The convenience of being able to source the majority of stock from a handful of suppliers, along with the corresponding efficiencies of stock intakes and paperwork, usually wins out and as a result most shops and restaurants will buy their stock from wholesalers.

One of the roles of a Food Hub is to try and provide the best of both worlds: eliminating the costs of the supply chain so that both producer and buyer get a fair deal, while also giving the buyer access to a range of products that makes it as convenient as possible for them to source their supplies.

An online trading platform is one way to achieve this. An online trading platform allows food producers and manufacturing businesses to upload their product availability to the internet and buyers can have a trading relationship with several producers through one convenient portal. When the buyer makes a purchase on the trading platform they are dealing directly with the producer.

Over the past decade there has been an explosion of web developers creating trading platforms for food. There was one that clearly stood out for us as being the right platform for the Cambridge Food Hub. This is the Open Food Network. Whereas many trading platforms have been developed using investment capital, and are therefore already wedded to the Capital and Growth way, the Open Food Network has very much grown out of the grassroots sustainable food movement, and is a values-driven not-for-profit company. The Open Food Network trading platform has been developed internationally, using open source software. In Cambridge, local shops, cafés and restaurants are now able to visit the Cambridge Food Hub 'shopfront' on the Open Food Network website and have a direct trading relationship with several local producers and local food manufacturing businesses, as well as some larger manufacturing companies from further afield which have strong ethical and environmental credentials. Although they are buying from several different companies, the buyer receives one compound invoice, which is much simpler to process, and receives the goods in one delivery.

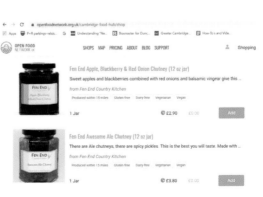

The Open Food Network is an online trading platform which facilitates direct trade with local food producers.

Delivery vehicles and supply chain coordination

In my opinion one of the shortfalls of many early attempts of connecting food buyers with producers via an online food trading platform was that they did not give due consideration to how order fulfilment was to happen after the trade had taken place; a sophisticated e-commerce site is all well and good, but at the end of the day local food supply chains rely on honest, hard-working people who roll their sleeves up and get on with loading and unloading vans, driving to farms to collect produce, packing veg boxes, collating wholesale orders and all the other manual tasks that are required to get food from A to B.

The Food Hub provides the workforce and vans necessary for aggregating the produce and products being distributed throughout the Local Food Ecosystem and also for collating and delivering buyers' orders. The vans are electric, and charge from photovoltaic cells on the roof of the Food Hub; one of the serendipitous factors that makes everything about the Local Food Ecosystem concept just fall into place is that when food is only being transported short distances it is possible to do this within the limited range of electric vehicles.

The unique value offered to the Local Food Ecosystem by the Food Hub is the innovative techniques of food supply chain coordination that were described in the last chapter: namely ensuring that all food finds a destination where it is valued and arranging ultra-efficient delivery routes in which resources can be cycled and social organisations can be served. Although the Local Food Ecosystem operates on a principle of self-organisation and freedom from control, many of the key benefits the Local Food Ecosystem is capable of delivering simply cannot happen without a person or organisation overseeing the whole system and managing the movement of resources. The supply chain coordination service provided by the Food Hub could be interpreted as a form of control, but it still fits within this ethos if it is considered as the role which the Food Hub plays in the functioning of the whole, and also when you factor in the ownership structure, which will be explained soon.

The Food Hub building

The final element of the Food Hub's offering is the physical space that hosts the various activities it performs. This is the Food Hub building. It is

The Green Coffee Shop Scheme has been a great way to illustrate the wider Local Food Ecosystem concept. It demonstrates how food miles are reduced by organising circular delivery routes and eliminating empty van miles, and also how the system makes it possible for resources, such as used coffee grounds, to be cycled when it otherwise wouldn't be economically viable to do so.

essentially a food storage and distribution centre, although it too has some novel and innovative features that set it apart from the type of building a conventional food distributor might operate from.

One of these features is a low-energy cold-store. Industrial cold-storage and refrigeration is yet to have its moment under the critical spotlight of the environmental movement, but I am sure its time will come; it is a massive problem. Many supermarkets and distribution centres include vast areas, sometimes acres of space, which are constantly refrigerated. Not only does this require significant amounts of energy, the chiller units use fluorinated gases to run. Hydrofluorocarbons have an equivalent greenhouse effect which is tens of thousands of times greater than that of carbon dioxide, and they leak. Refrigerated vehicles are also not great for the environment; the insulation and refrigeration equipment make the vehicle heavier, as well as reducing the load capacity, making chilled vehicles much less efficient. Refrigeration is obviously a very important aspect of food safety, as well as helping extend the shelf life of foods and reducing waste, of course. Even so, it is about time that attention was given to the problem of energy and refrigerant gas use in industrial food cold-storage.

The Food Hub has two answers to this problem. As is often the case, the best solution is often the simplest and most straightforward: eliminate the need for cold-storage. Why is refrigeration needed? Well, the two main reasons are food safety and extending the shelf life of food. Food safety is a very important consideration, of course, and I would never suggest that food safety should be compromised under any circumstances. However, the types of foods for which refrigeration is a food-safety necessity mainly fall into the meat, dairy or processed-food categories. These types of foods are not handled so much by the Food Hub, and so refrigeration becomes less important.

In transportation, refrigeration only really becomes necessary when food is covering long distances and spending a long time in transit. Here we see yet another example of how keeping things local simplifies things no end; in a Local Food Ecosystem, where food travels very short distances and can reach its destination quickly, most types of produce can survive the journey unrefrigerated without there being any deterioration in its quality whatsoever. This means that the Food Hub's vehicles do not have to be refrigerated, and the small number of products which do need to be kept chilled can be transported in insulated cases.

Fresh food being stored at the Food Hub building does need to be kept cool. The brief for the cold-store in the Food Hub is that it should be low-energy, and not use fluorinated gases. Constructing a cellar is one way to achieve this; an underground cellar is completely passive in terms of energy use, of course. The downside to an underground cellar is that it takes effort and energy to bring food up and down from the cellar; something that is going to make day-to-day operations less efficient. The solution opted for instead is to use heat-pump technology. The heat pump extracts energy from the ground beneath the cold-store, cooling it down, and then uses that energy elsewhere in the building where heat is required, such as the offices, or to heat water.

The opportunity to showcase an alternative method for chilled storage of food is something that especially excites me about the Food Hub project as it is something which I believe has the potential to go on and become a very impactful innovation in its own right. Could we one day see restaurants using heat pumps to simultaneously chill their food and heat the dining area? Or supermarkets using heat-exchange technology to chill their store rooms and heat their offices, or even the 'warm air curtain' which invites you in on a cold day?

Another significant feature of the Food Hub building is incubator kitchen units. An important element of the Local Food Ecosystem concept is small-business creation, especially food-processing businesses which use locally grown foods as their raw ingredients, and even more so, businesses who can fulfil the 'flexible food user' role that is so vital to the functioning of the Local Food Ecosystem. The Food Hub building includes kitchen units that are available to small food businesses on favourable terms. A business occupying one of these units benefits from being able to access their ingredients from the same building, *and* having their finished products dispatched to local shops and restaurants via the Food Hub's distribution service, or direct to customers via the box scheme.

I can envision a time in the future, when the Food Hub is established, when several small food-manufacturing businesses are operating from the Food Hub's incubator kitchens, a number of which make products that are suitable for selling in jars. They have all decided to adopt the same kind of reusable jar, and there is a continuous process in operation whereby the empty jars are collected from shops and home-delivery customers and then brought back to Food Hub, where they are cleansed and returned to circulation. Materials are saved, and the businesses save money on packaging. It is eminently possible.

The kitchens also help the Food Hub to fulfil some of the other social benefits which were originally intended for it: when used as a training kitchen this part of the Food Hub can be used to pass on food-preparation skills to schoolchildren, disadvantaged families, or young people hoping to start a career in the catering industry. From here the ethos of the Local Food Ecosystem, and knowledge about sustainable dietary choices and practices, can permeate to other areas of the food system. There is great potential for Food Hubs as centres for education as well as food distribution.

The Food Hub is designed as a multi-functional facility, with flexible-use spaces that can be used for different activities. The main hall will predominantly be used for packing veg boxes and collating orders. However, at times when it is not being used for this purpose, such as evenings and weekends, it can be reconfigured to become a venue for other events and activities; these could be charitable dining events, conferences, live music, farmers' markets, surplus food redistribution gatherings, private parties – anything, really, where a large open-plan space could be put to good use.

Naturally, environmental sustainability is an important aspect of the design brief, and the building design features sustainable building materials, renewable energy and rain/grey water harvesting systems.

A less obvious but in many ways even more important aspect of the design brief is that the building needs to be an environment which nurtures human well-being. The workspace must be a place that simply *feels right* to exist within; something that can be achieved with natural lighting, good acoustics, and an architectural design which follows the principles of geometry and proportion which are themselves principles of Harmony.[6]

A concept image for the interior of the Food Hub. This should be a space that enhances the well-being of the people who dwell within it.

Putting the principles into practice

So far I have described the physical processes of the Food Hub: the things it does and the facilities it provides. But what about the business model that underpins it? The Local Food Ecosystem was conceived as a business system which conforms to a 'new way' economic model;

---

6. Refer to 'The Golden Thread', Chapter 3 of *Harmony: A New Way of Looking at Our World* (see note 1, Chapter 1).

one in which purpose is a higher priority than profit and which exists to serve ecological and anthropocentric needs rather than material needs. The Food Hub has also been designed as a business which conforms to the new way economic model. In some ways this makes it even more exciting, for while the Local Food Ecosystem is a concept, the Food Hub is an actual, tangible enterprise. We find ourselves at the frontier of a potentially very exciting episode in commercial history, where new companies are being formed that adhere to new economic models and have principles of Harmony as their foundation. If these companies prove themselves to be successful, and thereby demonstrate that a new way is indeed possible, then this could be profound for the future of industry and commerce and its effect on the planet.

In designing a new way economic model company, or 'Harmony business' (such as for the Food Hub), we need to refer back to the guidelines in Chapter 2. To recap, the key characteristics of a Harmony business are:

- It would be founded on principles of Harmony.
- It would have, as its primary objective, a noble purpose.
- It would deliver benefit to all of its stakeholders in equitable measure.

The first thing to do is define the noble purpose. In doing this we need to think carefully about exactly what the unmet need is, and what the specific value is that our Food Hub is going to bring to the community.

The noble purpose of the Local Food Ecosystem is: *feeding people with healthy and sustainably produced food.*

This is something that is undeniably a good thing and that is of genuine value to society. However, the Food Hub is not the Local Food Ecosystem and it needs a noble purpose of its own. If a fully functioning Local Food Ecosystem is to be of such benefit, but needs support in order to be able to operate, then the provision of this support will also be a noble pursuit. This helps us to understand what is required of the Food Hub, its reason for being, which is to support the functioning of the Local Food Ecosystem. Finally we need to place this purpose within a framework that considers the social and environmental factors we are aiming to achieve, resulting in a noble purpose for our Food Hub that reads like this:

> *To facilitate and coordinate the supply chain within the Local Food Ecosystem in a way that minimises waste, minimises environmental impact, and supports a vibrant local food economy that is accessible to all.*

This then becomes the mission statement for the company.

The purpose of the Local Food Ecosystem is to feed people with healthy and sustainably produced food.

Ownership

Another of the key characteristics of a Harmony business is that is should deliver benefit to all its stakeholders in equitable measure. Owners, employees, suppliers, customers, society and the environment should all benefit to some degree from the existence of the organisation. More importantly, none of these stakeholders should be exploited for the benefit of another.

There is one approach to business ownership which is entirely in keeping with this philosophy and almost automatically achieves this objective. Quite simply, it is when the owners of the business are themselves the members of the other stakeholder groups; the owners of the company are the members of the Local Food Ecosystem and the employees. The shares in the company can be held on behalf of the members by an ownership trust. I shall describe this as 'distributed ownership'.

When the key stakeholders are also the owners of the business, this means that it always operates in the best interests of the Ecosystem that it serves, without being compromised by the need to generate profit for its shareholders. The imperative to make money is less of a factor because the owners of the company derive their value from the company primarily through the services it provides.

As we have already discussed, just because profit isn't the *primary* objective of the company doesn't preclude it from being *an* objective. Performing its operations free of the obligation to maximise profitability means it will be able to provide a competitive service and, paradoxically, be profitable. If and when dividends are paid out, that money goes back to its stakeholders: local growers, small food start-ups, local independent shops, and the employees of the company, of course. That money might be invested in new farming equipment or product development, or it might simply be considered additional motivation or reward for participating in the Ecosystem and working hard. Crucially, that money is being kept *within* the system; it is not extracted in a way that causes imbalance.

This ownership model goes a long way towards achieving the 'holy grail' of being a business which provides value to its owners, employees, customers, suppliers, society and the environment in equitable measure; the employees, customers and suppliers are also the owners. But there are two stakeholder groups that are less easy to represent as owners: society and the environment. The interests of society are represented in the mission statement. Increasing accessibility to healthy and sustainably produced food and supporting local economies is a benefit to society.

As for the environment, well, I would have to begin by saying that no commercial activity is *beneficial* to the environment. I once saw a TV show in which a celebrity described her hybrid 4-wheel-drive Lexus as 'totally environmentally friendly'. No it isn't. Not even slightly. It is not environmentally friendly; it is just less damaging to the environment than its petrol-powered counterpart. By this same rationale, I could not put my hand on my heart and claim that the Food Hub business model actually *benefits* the environment. However, by minimising wastage, by minimising food miles, by operating electric vehicles and encouraging sustainable farming practices we can at least claim that the business model has minimal environmental impact.

Membership-based revenue model

Early on in this chapter I made a reference to 'reduced costs, achieved the right way'. There are both good ways and bad ways to reduce costs. Cost cutting in the Capital and Growth way usually has bad connotations associated with it. Cuts are often motivated by the impetus to maximise profit. The costs which are cut might be people's jobs or wages. It is the obsession with cost cutting that has led to increasingly unsustainable farming methods.

The types of costs being cut in the Local Food Ecosystem are transportation costs, profit margins added by intermediaries, losses incurred when food goes to waste, energy used for refrigeration, and the enabling of refillable packaging schemes to happen. Processes are streamlined and the things which are being cut are the superfluities which have crept into the system and which are simply unnecessary when dealing with things on a local scale. These are good cuts to be making. The über-efficient supply chain coordination techniques employed by the Food Hub should make it *the* most cost-effective way of getting food from farm to user. Theoretically, food sourced through the Local Food Ecosystem should be the least expensive food available.

This is not the case, of course; much of the food that comes through the industrial channels is so mind-bogglingly cheap it leaves you baffled as to how it is even possible. It is because many of the costs have been externalised, making it artificially cheap and unfairly competitive. But that is what the situation is and there is not much we can do about it.

These are good cuts to be making. The über-efficient supply chain coordination techniques employed by the Food Hub should make it the most cost-effective way of getting food from farm to user.

Even so, the cutting of costs through ultra-efficient supply chain management is perhaps the most advantageous aspect of the Local Food Ecosystem concept. The benefit that it brings is that it makes local and sustainably produced food as reasonably priced as it is possible to be. Maybe not as cheap as the industrial stuff, but at least brought to within an acceptable tolerance. The significance of this is that it can be the difference between viability and otherwise for independent, local food businesses. Given half a chance, local food could become a burgeoning market sector, with the knock-on effect that this encourages more people to start local food businesses and more farmers to consider marketing their produce locally.

For this to be the case, for the cost of distributing food through the Food Hub to truly be the lowest possible option, the Food Hub cannot be adding any costs of its own; it should only get enough to cover its operational costs. But those operational costs *do* need to be met, of course.

The revenue model for the Food Hub also needs to be one that allows it to perform its operations without them being influenced or compromised by financial considerations; the socially and environmentally beneficial functions must be allowed to happen unabated otherwise the whole thing is pointless. And for this to be the case it is critical that the revenue stream for the Food Hub be completely distinct from the food it is handling. Think back to the analogy of the BBC and how it is able to deliver impartial, high-quality and distinctive output to all audiences through virtue of keeping its funding distinct from its offering. It should also be remembered that the Food Hub is facilitating *direct* trade between the members of the Local Food Ecosystem. The Food Hub is not a trader of food itself, it is not 'buying' food and then 'selling' it at a profit, and this is a fundamentally important aspect of the entire ethos. Instead, the Food Hub is a provider of food services.

Coming up with a revenue model for the Food Hub that meets these criteria has been a considerable challenge, and one that still needs a bit of work. Even so, the revenue model which best fits with the concept is a membership-based revenue model: the operational costs of the Food Hub are divided fairly between the fee-paying members of the Local Food Ecosystem. Members of the Local Food Ecosystem have access to the full range of Food Hub services for a set membership fee.

Although the membership of the Local Food Ecosystem includes both buyers and sellers of food, it is the buyers who bear the operational costs of the business through membership fees. The obligation of the sellers is that they commit to selling their goods at 'direct' prices.

A significant benefit for fee-paying Food Hub members is *direct trade*: the ability to purchase goods for the same price they would pay if they were to turn up at the farm or the factory in a big van and buy a pallet-load of goods. Typically, this price will be around 30 per cent less than if the goods were bought from a wholesaler. With a set membership fee there is a break-even point: the point at which the cost of membership equals the savings that are made by buying direct. For example, a 25kg sack of quinoa that costs £100 from a wholesaler would only cost £70 bought direct from the producer. If the membership fee paid by the buyer is £30 then the cost of the sack through the Local Food Ecosystem is also £100; it is exactly at the break-even point. However, if the buyer were to purchase two sacks of quinoa the total cost would be £200 from the wholesaler, but only £170 when purchased direct with a set membership fee. As long as the members use the service to a greater extent than the break-even point they are quids in.

To help understand the distributed-ownership and membership-based revenue model better, consider this analogy.

Imagine a head chef in a top restaurant. I'm sure this chef would like nothing more than to be able to get up at 7 o'clock in the morning, hop into a van and drive around half a dozen local farms collecting freshly picked cherry tomatoes, freshly cut kale and freshly dug potatoes, then take them back to the kitchen where they would be the ingredients that are used during the day. Aside from ensuring that they got the freshest possible produce, they would also be paying less by buying direct from the producer. Doing this is completely impractical, of course; the time and cost of doing that run outweighs the price advantage gained over buying from a wholesaler. Now, suppose our chef were to club together with half a dozen other chefs. Between them they buy a van, and then employ a driver to go and pick up the produce on their behalf. Now that collection run is much more worthwhile, not least because the operational costs are shared seven ways.

The driver of the van is going to be content as long as their wages are paid and the van is safe and legal to drive with enough fuel for the journey. These are the set costs that the chefs have to pay. Beyond that, the driver doesn't really mind if they are being sent out to collect £200 worth of potatoes or £2,000 worth of samphire. The point is that, having made that investment, it is in the best interests of our consortium of chefs to deploy this resource as effectively as possible, and you can rest assured that they will be sending their driver on the errands that save them the most money.

In this analogy the collective ownership of the van is the equivalent of the distributed ownership of the Food Hub business, and the wages of the driver and van running costs are the equivalent of the operational costs that are paid for by membership fees. Just as our hypothetical consortium of chefs do, it is expected that the fee-paying members of the Local Food Ecosystem will behave in way that maximises the value for money they get from their membership.

Like the van driver in the analogy, the Food Hub is happy as long as its operational costs are covered; it is providing a service, not trading food, so the value of those goods is in many ways immaterial. This revenue strategy leads to yet another advantageous situation: by paying a set fee the savings for the buyer are greater the more they purchase, and this incentivises buyers to purchase more from other members of the Local Food Ecosystem. If they are savvy enough to exploit the service to their advantage, then so much the better; this simply means that more local trade is taking place and more local food is consumed in the Food Hub's area. The very objective we are hoping to achieve.

Small-scale, artisanal food enterprises and market gardeners who do not produce goods in the sort of volume that leads to a 'distributor' rate are allowed to sell at 'wholesale' rate (the rate that shops normally buy for) instead, and the obligation on their part is that they exclusively sell their goods through the trading platform. In this case, the value that the fee-paying members get is not a cost saving, but is access to locally produced artisanal products that aren't available anywhere else, and also the convenience of being able to trade with several small businesses through one portal. On the face of it this may lessen the justification of the membership fee; now buyers are being asked to pay a fee in order to obtain products which the producer would have previously brought to them without an additional charge (albeit at considerable cost to the producer). In this instance the buyers are asked to consider the bigger picture: having several small businesses, each making a number of short journeys delivering relatively small quantities of products, is not efficient or good for the environment. Also, by creating conditions in which it is viable for new artisanal food businesses to start up, the buyers are nurturing an industry sector that is able to supply them with distinctive, good-quality local products, products that cannot be purchased from their corporate competitors. The set membership fee gives the buyer access both to goods which are available at 'distributor rate', and therefore come with a cost saving, and to goods which are available at 'wholesale rate', but not available anywhere else. It is up to the buyer to choose which goods they purchase, and if they purchase wisely it is possible to buy more than enough 'distributor rate' goods for the savings to outweigh the membership fee. If the set fee has been paid anyway, and is justified through savings on other products, then the buyer is no better or worse off than they were before with regard to buying goods from the smaller-scale artisanal businesses at wholesale rate.

Incidentally, if I were mentoring a small business, as I occasionally do, I would normally advise them against entering into any form of exclusivity arrangement. This situation is different, however. Agreeing to sell their goods exclusively on the trading platform does not restrict who they can sell to, it just means that they commit to using the trading platform as their sole avenue for business-to-business sales. And these businesses get an astonishingly good deal in return for this small commitment; the Food Hub provides storage space for their stock, will collect and deliver goods on their behalf, and takes care of invoicing and payment collection, all at no cost to the producer. It is precisely the scenario I described earlier in the chapter, when I talked about the hypothetical cordial-making business and how the ability to get a relatively small quantity of product delivered to the buyer without incurring costs would be the difference between having a viable business and not. The thing is, we *need* businesses like this if we are to have the vibrant local food economy we so desire.

An important feature of the membership-based revenue model is that it enables the total cost of food to be varied at different levels within the Local Food Ecosystem; members pay a different membership rate depending on their role in the functioning of the Ecosystem. This is an important aspect of the way in which the Local Food Ecosystem achieves its social and environmental purposes. Food users who require the highest levels of service have the greatest membership fees. Food users who can be flexible with regard to their inputs, and therefore enable the 'zero-food-waste' objective to be fulfilled, have lower membership fees. There is also

A collaborative approach: representatives from the local council, the university, anti-poverty organisations and the food industry come together to address the issue of food poverty in the 'Good Food for All' workshop.

a category of food users that fulfil the 'Good Food for All'[7] role within the Local Food Ecosystem, for whom membership is free.

The free membership afforded to the Good Food for All food users should not be thought of as a charitable gesture. In a natural ecosystem *all* components of the ecosystem are vital to its functioning and there is no hierarchy of importance; the apex predator is no more or less important than the bacteria which decompose its faeces. In the Local Food Ecosystem the poshest restaurant in town is no more or less important than the soup kitchen operated by the volunteer group. The Local Food Ecosystem exists to provide the right type of service for each of them. Part of the value that the higher membership fee-paying members of the Local Food Ecosystem are buying into is an ethical supply chain that minimises waste and environmental impact and improves access to healthy fresh produce for people who are on a low income. The services provided by the Good Food for All members are vital to the functioning of the Local Food Ecosystem and the achievement of these key objectives. Regarding Good Food for All organisations in this way results in a far greater solution to the problem of food poverty than the measures which are currently in place. Rather than keeping food

---

7. 'Good Food for All' is a category of membership specifically aimed at organisations or initiatives which make good-quality, healthy food more accessible to low-income segments of the community.

poverty apart from the commercial food industry and in the realm of the charitable sector (reliant on food donations, financial donations and volunteer workers), the Local Food Ecosystem is inclusive, offering a systemic and self-sustaining solution.

The revenue-based membership model has probably been the most difficult aspect of the business model to explain to people. 'What is wrong with simply adding a margin like everyone else does, and just using the profits to pay for the social and environmental deeds?' Well, for starters, no matter how transparent the pricing is, and how altruistic the deeds performed with the profits are, this is still a Capital and Growth business model. This is no different to a business which promises that '50 per cent of all profits go to charity'; nothing wrong with that, but when the company is not making profit, then no money is going to charity. With the Local Food Ecosystem the social and environmental activities must be performed week in and week out; it's a whole system, it can't simply start and stop functioning depending on how well the business is performing.

I can also categorically tell you from good honest experience that the profit margin approach is not going to work. The Cambridge Organic Food Company has been wholesaling organic fresh produce in the conventional way for over twenty years, and this operation has never been profitable enough to do anything more than the basics. It is incredibly hard to make a profit buying and selling organic fruit and veg. The profit margin added means the produce is only really appropriate for a handful of specialist local shops, and you must factor in the risks associated with trading in perishable goods. This might sound like a reason for suggesting that the membership-based revenue model isn't going to work either; after all if you can't make it work with the tried and tested 'for-profit' way, how on earth do I know it is going to work with an unorthodox and untried approach? The honest truth is that I don't, but as I said at the very beginning of the book, we have to at least give it a try. Even so, there are some features of the membership-based revenue model which ought to give it a better chance of achieving the social and environmental operations than the 'profit-margin' model.

The chief flaw with the profit-margin model is that it is reliant on sales and profits to consistently deliver the extra revenue required to run the operations which bring social and environmental benefit, whereas in a real-life competitive market volume of sales is never guaranteed, buyers can and will negotiate on price, and generally market forces squeeze the profit to the leanest possible point (at least, this is what tends to happen with fresh produce wholesale). In the membership-based revenue model the operational costs, including the costs of providing the socially and environmentally beneficial operations, are covered, no matter what, by the set membership fee, but the buyers have an opportunity to make their membership fee work to their advantage simply by making sure their orders are above the break-even point. Essentially, this revenue model exchanges the opportunity to make profit when the going is good for a robust and reliable income stream which enables the innovative supply chain coordination techniques to take effect. Ironically, in this scenario the buyers are likely to be putting in the kind of orders that would have had the profit-margin business model supplier rubbing their hands together with glee. Indeed, we have seen this pattern of ordering from the Food Hub's early adopters already, inspiring confidence that the new model will work.

The notion of the socially and environmentally beneficial operations being paid for as an extra expense to the 'commercial' operations is completely wrong, of course, as is hopefully quite clear at this stage in the book. The idea that they might be paid for out of profits from an otherwise commercially viable activity is not in keeping with the underlying philosophy. The Local Food Ecosystem concept is based on the principle of the **whole**; paying for socially and environmentally beneficial operations out of profits would essentially mean they are being considered separately from the main operations, when this categorically isn't the case. Consider the example of a typical Food Hub operation that I gave earlier in the book, when the Food Hub van goes on a delivery round to eight establishments, of which the first seven are shops who are receiving deliveries of goods and are also having some unsold surplus food taken away, and the eighth delivery is to a community fridge where the donated food is dropped off. We are certainly not going to make the community fridge pay anything for this service. The trip to the community fridge is, if anything, part of the service offered to the shops; it enables them to be more responsible regarding what happens to their waste. The cost of performing this delivery round, therefore, should be divided seven ways (between the shops only) rather than eight. And the cost of the trip to the community fridge should not be considered as a 'charitable surcharge' added to the membership fee either; the shops should get enough value from their membership anyway. Because both the collection of the donated food and the delivery to the community fridge have been incorporated into the delivery round in the most efficient manner, the cost of doing this is fairly negligible; certainly in comparison to the alternative, which is sending a van around to do the collections and delivery on a run that is independent of other activities. At this stage you might ask: 'if the cost of doing that is negligible why can't that be done in the profit-margin model?'. There is absolutely no reason why it can't. In fact, it's such an easy and obviously beneficial operation, I wonder why food wholesalers up and down the country are not doing it already. But the thing is, done like this it is an altruistic gesture on the part of the wholesaler, rather than a systematic solution which fully integrates this activity into the **whole**, including the cost of doing it. And the other thing to remember is that the community fridge delivery is only one example of the kind of activity undertaken by the Local Food Ecosystem. A fully functional Local Food Ecosystem will constitute a multitude of interconnections and operations, a nexus of activity, in which the socially and environmentally beneficial activities are intertwined with the more commercially orientated ones. There is no separation between the two, and it would be impossible to tease apart the respective costs.

The membership-based revenue model, in which operational costs are kept distinct from the goods handled, also makes it easier for organisations who are indirect beneficiaries of the system to contribute towards its operation. An example of an indirect beneficiary might be the health service, who will benefit from having the cost of diet-related ill health mitigated through better access to healthy fresh food throughout the community. Such stakeholders may be able to contribute towards the operations of the Local Food Ecosystem by participating in 'multi-way value exchanges'. These exchanges could be financial – a direct contribution to the operational costs of the Food Hub which helps fund the provision of service to Good Food for All members – or they could be non-financial – the health service could participate in a healthy-diet-prescribing scheme which sends people in the direction of the Food Hub, for example. In many ways, it is the non-financial value exchanges that are the more exciting and the most valuable.

In a similar vein, the membership-based revenue model does give organisations an opportunity to contribute altruistically if they so wish. Even though I said it shouldn't be considered that the membership fee includes a 'charitable' element (due to the fact that the fee can be easily justified through savings), that doesn't mean that fee-paying members cannot join simply to contribute towards and participate in something which is good for society. Indeed, there may be a category of membership in which the member *does not* fully justify the cost of membership through savings but pays their membership anyway to demonstrate social and environmental responsibility. I imagine such members may be corporate clients, who might order just a small amount of fruit and snacks for the staff canteen and have the grounds from the office coffee machine taken away, but still consider the membership fee worthwhile. A key selling point of the membership fee is that it supports an ethical supply chain. Whereas the financial benefits will be very important to local independent businesses in addition to demonstrating an ethical supply chain, I'd like to think that there are also some larger companies and organisations who will participate in and support the functioning of the Local Food Ecosystem simply because they can.

Calculating membership fees ought to be a straightforward matter of working out the cost of running the operation and dividing that figure between the number of members according to a formula which differentiates the fee depending on whether they are a 'demanding', 'flexible' or 'Good Food for All' food user. That is the theory, at least. In practice, this has been quite challenging. The thing is, the Local Food Ecosystem needs to be well established and stable before these kinds of calculations can happen. Working out what the fees should be when you are in the process of setting up the Local Food Ecosystem is much harder. In the early stages it can be difficult to justify membership fees without there being a decent range of goods available on the trading platform. I would love to be able to give you the solution to this 'chicken and egg' conundrum but we are still in the process of figuring it out in Cambridge ourselves. But figure it out we will, so make sure you read the second edition of this book when it comes out.

One of the challenges we have encountered with regard to membership fees is that buyers struggle to factor the fee into their calculations when trying to work out how to price things up. My answer to this is that it is better to consider the fee as an overhead, rather than a component of the cost of the goods, as this next analogy should explain.

Imagine the owner of a farm shop on the outskirts of the city. They are keen to stock their shop with distinctive, locally produced foods. They realise that by visiting the farms in person they can get fresher produce, find products that are hard to obtain from the usual suppliers, and buy goods for less money than from a wholesaler. Every Monday they hop into their van and do a tour of the county, visiting four farms and five small manufacturing businesses. The shop is now stocked with a glorious selection of local foods which have been priced up according to the price paid to the producers. The van's running costs and the shop owner's time isn't factored into the pricing of each item (although I would expect the shop to put a higher percentage mark-up than is added to goods which have been delivered rather than collected); they are instead considered overheads of running the business. The Food Hub is essentially providing the same service, only it can do it much more cost-effectively. The membership fee should also be considered as an overhead.

The distributed-ownership model means that the members themselves should be asked to contribute to the fee calculation process.

The final point to make about membership fees is, as you may have already figured out for yourself, that membership fees will lessen the more members that there are. As with everything else that the Food Hub does to try and improve local trading conditions and stimulate new business creation, this will hopefully initiate a snowball effect that leads to a burgeoning local food economy.

Hybrid business model

Running a business which only covers its operational costs is all well and good; operational costs are always covered, so it is a robust and sustainable business model. However, operating in this non-profit-making manner does limit the impact potential of the venture. I did say at the beginning of the book that the Food Hub is, first and foremost, a *business*. Being able to generate revenue over and above the operational costs allows for reinvestment, or it could reward and motivate employees and other stakeholders. Critically it all comes down to 'success'; regardless of how you decide to quantify success, the fact of the matter is that a 'successful' enterprise is going to be considerably more impactful because when something is proven to be successful it is far easier to convince other people that the concept is worth pursuing.

So how can the Food Hub achieve revenue over and above its operational costs when only covering operational costs is such a fundamental aspect of the entire concept?

This is where I would like to introduce the concept of the 'hybrid business model': two business operations existing alongside each other in a mutually beneficial way, one of which operates purely for the greater good on a non-profit-making basis, the other operating on a more conventional profit-making basis.

The Food Hub distribution and supply chain coordination service should only ever aspire to cover its operational costs. The whole purpose of this service is to stimulate a vibrant and burgeoning local food economy, and the Food Hub receiving more from the Local Food Ecosystem than its basic costs compromises this very important objective.

However, the Food Hub does have an opportunity to make a profit by also selling products directly to members of the public, through retail. Food Hub buildings offer a unique opportunity for an authentic and distinctive food shopping experience. They are the places where growers and artisanal food-processing businesses convene with their goods, making it a venue which offers shoppers unprecedented access to local food. Because the goods are sourced at direct prices there is an opportunity to make a healthy margin when retailing those goods. Although this might appear to contradict the ethos of the whole concept, selling at the full retail price is actually the right thing to do as selling at a lower price would undercut the independent retailers who are also sourcing goods through the Local Food Ecosystem. Also, as much as the Food Hub is about improving accessibility to good food, it is also not about driving down prices and initiating a 'race to the bottom'. When it comes to food I am a big believer in *appropriate* pricing; too cheap and the farmer is being squeezed too much and production values will fall. In a functioning Local Food Ecosystem, systemic costs will have been cut so that both the Food Hub and local independent retailers can sell local food at reasonable prices, and there will always be Good Food for

All programmes which improve access to food for people who struggle to afford it.

In Cambridge, the retail operation that sits alongside the Food Hub is the already well-established Cambridge Organic Food Company vegetable box scheme. I would suggest that other local organic box schemes throughout the UK would also make excellent starting points around which to build Food Hub enterprises.

If the retail side of the business operates on a for-profit basis can it still be considered a Harmony business?

I would say yes. The retail operation shares the same noble purpose as the Local Food Ecosystem, and it also meets the objective of creating benefit for owners, employees, suppliers, customers, society and the environment in equitable measure. No stakeholder is being exploited, so all profit is 'sustainable profit'.

The Food Hub is able to offer people good local food, at a reasonable price, with exceptionally high ethical values. This sounds to me like a recipe for business success.

The Local Food Ecosystem is a business system which operates purely for the greater good. This brings a considerable advantage to the commercial arm of the company, as it endows the products and services provided with an extraordinarily high ethical rating. I believe that 'ethical consumerism' will become an increasingly important aspect of spending behaviour in years to come. People will see the incredibly good things that the Food Hub is doing for the environment and for society and will want to support that business. However, they will not be able to if the Food Hub is only providing business to business services. Selling to the public in addition to the services which enable the functioning of the Local Food Ecosystem means that the Food Hub is able to offer people good local food, at a reasonable price, with exceptionally high ethical values. This sounds to me like a recipe for business success.

Conclusion

The Food Hub is a purpose-driven business. Its main objective is to create the conditions in which independent local food businesses can thrive, which in turn leads to a prosperous local food economy that can be managed in a way that best serves the needs of people and has the smallest environmental impact.

The membership-based revenue model keeps the operational costs of running the business distinct from the products being distributed. The importance of this is that it means economic considerations do not influence the way the supply chain is managed; the Local Food Ecosystem can function at optimum efficiency, delivering the social and environmental objectives without compromise.

The membership fee basically pays for the Food Hub van to arrive, periodically, at the buyer's establishment. The van can bring goods which have been purchased directly from local producers at direct prices, and also take goods away. It is up to the member to decide upon the extent to which they use that service, but the value of membership increases the more that it is used, which is great because it incentivises local trade.

What the Local Food Ecosystem means to me: Heather Sturman

Heather Sturman runs her own small food business, Fen End Country Kitchen, in which she manufactures a range of distinctive preserves and chutneys. Here, Heather tells us how using the Food Hub to distribute her products has enabled her to grow the business.

Fen End Country Kitchen was brought to life in November 2014 in my Cambridgeshire kitchen. My previous life had been as a primary school teacher which I gave up when starting a family in 2008. Needing a fresh stimulus once my son began school, I started making preserves as gifts and then as fundraisers to support local charities in which I was involved. By the start of 2014, I wondered if my preserving might take off as a little business which would fit around family life. I approached a couple of local farm shops and sold my goods through local artisanal markets. Fortunately, I seemed to be creating preserves which were slightly unusual and incredibly well received. Within my limits, Fen End Country Kitchen grew successfully over the next few years. As mid-2019 approached, I realised I needed to make a decision about the direction of my business. With a more independent child, I had more time on my hands to re-model Fen End Country Kitchen. Should I continue with stalls at local markets, such as the one my husband and I set up in our village with some other small, local producers in 2016, or should I focus more on the volume of production and try to increase my wholesale market? Whilst our 'local hub' (our village market) had proved a success, I had saturated the local area. I couldn't really move the business forwards without some significant changes.

Fortuitously, therefore, it was in May 2019 that I met Duncan Catchpole to talk about his latest brainchild, the Cambridge Sustainable Food Hub. Having known Duncan for many years via Cambridge Organic Food Company, I was excited to hear about his most recent project, knowing it would be ethically and environmentally sound, both of which ring true for me.

It didn't take much convincing for me to sign up to be a part of the Food Hub adventure as one of their small food producers. It simply made perfect sense not purely in terms of all the stakeholders but, in particular, as a tiny drop in the jammy/sticky ocean of national preserve-making companies, I could see how it could give Fen End Country Kitchen a route into other local retail outlets that I couldn't manage to reach single-handedly. Having my products advertised by the Hub, ordered via their website and then coordinated into one purchase request has simplified logistics and increased my presence in the market via local independent cafés, delis and other foodie jewels. My production has increased significantly at no increased cost to me, since the Food Hub does not currently levy any additional charge. My business is becoming increasingly viable financially.

The network of food businesses involved in the Hub has also provided me with the benefit of purchasing some hard-to-come-by or bulk ingredients which are local and seasonal. This has been particularly useful during the challenges of 2020. I can contact retailers directly to order, the Food Hub staff collect my goods on their usual runs and pass on to me on my delivery day. No extra food miles and two happy businesses!

Another significantly positive aspect of the Food Hub is that all my deliveries are taken care of by Duncan's team. For over 20 years, I have had a fruit and veg box delivered by COFCO. Now, the weekly arrival of my box by the cheery-faced driver signals the pick-up of my preserves heading ecologically soundly (COFCO has several electric vehicles) to the Food Hub, where they are sorted and distributed to their onward retail destinations. This has been an incredible boon for a micro-business. I have always struggled with the time and money involved in making deliveries. Previously, I had to impose a minimum order or add a delivery charge, neither of which accounted for the costs I incurred and my lost time in the kitchen. I couldn't manage to pay myself a minimum wage, let alone a living wage for the hours that slipped away.

This distribution model has allowed me to scale up my business whilst focussing on the product, rather than logistics. The range of outlets which stock my preserves has also grown to include those which I would not have otherwise come across, thus giving me a wider geographical reach.

During the last year, I have been able to increase my production to full capacity. I am now able to think about the next stage in the business; I have viable choices.

In short, the Food Hub has been invaluable in giving my business new life and the opportunity to grow organically. I have been able to maintain my ethos of home-made preserves using as many as possible locally sourced and seasonal ingredients, whilst expanding my market into a growing number of smaller, independent outlets, with all the ecological benefits. Preserving (pun intended!) our local food ecosystems, small business and our world ... Food Hubs all the way!

Heather Sturman

In addition to distributing her products through the Food Hub, Heather sells directly at farmers' markets and country fairs.

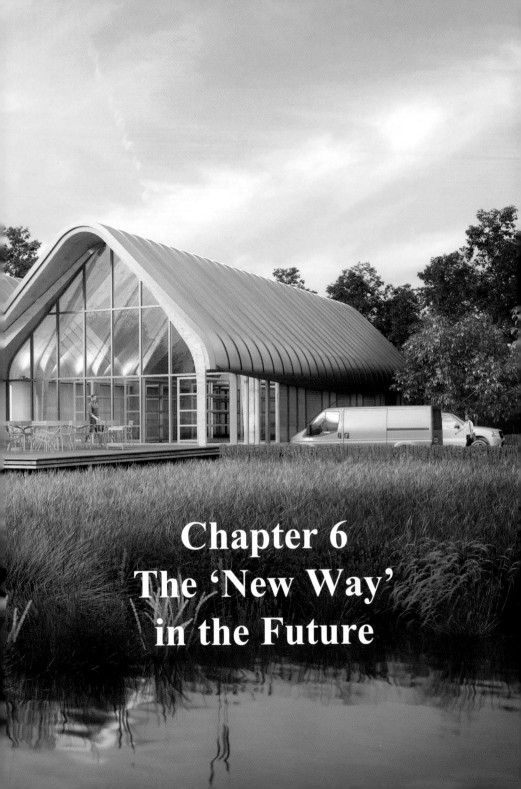

Chapter 6
The 'New Way'
in the Future

Chapter 6
The 'New Way' in the Future

Now that I have shared the vision for both the Local Food Ecosystem and the Food Hub with you I'm going spend this final chapter fantasising about how the world might look in the future if the Local Food Ecosystem concept takes off.

One day in the future

Allow me to project myself a decade or so into the future. It's a beautiful sunny morning in the early summer and I am about to set off on a journey to Preston as I have been invited to give a talk about the Local Food Ecosystem at the Preston Food Hub. I have decided to travel by car on this occasion so that I can take a scenic route and check out one or two other Food Hubs along the way. I drive an electric car, of course; it is a single seater that I have picked up from the local transport hub. It only weighs 600kg but is perfectly safe and comfortable on long journeys.

Before setting off on my journey I decide to have a hearty breakfast in a café close to home that I particularly like. They are members of the Cambridge Local Food Ecosystem and much of the food they buy comes directly from local farms. This café has a reputation for making sublime porridge, using local oats, with a choice of toppings. I opt for local honey and strawberries.

As I drive along some of the country roads out of Cambridgeshire, I note that the landscape has changed slightly from the way I remembered it ten years ago. There are many more farms which have diversified into horticultural crops for the local market, who now proudly boast about the quality of their produce with signs by their farm gates: 'The sweetest sweetcorn from Rectory Farm', 'Maypole Organics; specialists in organic salads and herbs', 'You ain't never tasted as good as Barney's spuds'.

The first Food Hub I visit on my journey is the one at Coventry. It is located fairly close to the organic gardens at Ryton. It was built around four years ago and is three times the size of the original Cambridge Food Hub. The Coventry Food Hub both distributes local food to local businesses and delivers food to private households. They operate a fleet of twelve electric vans, and pack and deliver around three thousand veg boxes each week. The thing I have come to see today is their retail operation, a truly magnificent food hall that has to be seen to be believed. As soon as you enter you are channelled through a corridor of fresh produce displays six feet high on either side. It is the epitome of abundance. Around 80 per cent of the produce has come from local farms, although there are some organic bananas, citrus fruits and other items which have come from further afield.

One of the things that strikes me the most is the amazing *diversity* of the produce on display. Most of it has come from small producers who have specialised in growing heritage varieties; a collaboration with Garden Organic led to a programme encouraging local growers to try growing different varieties of fruit and vegetables and widen the biodiversity of commercial crops, something they were much more confident in doing knowing it would all find a good home through the Local Food Ecosystem. There are no fewer than twelve different varieties of tomatoes on display, crystal apple cucumbers, golden, cylindrical and Chioggia beetroot, a choice of four different-coloured French beans, endive, chicory; you name it, it's there, along with many more things you've never heard of before. And the most remarkable thing about this display? Not a bit of it goes to waste. By mid-afternoon two thirds of it has been sold to customers. Shoppers know that if they come a little later in the day there will not be as much left, but that they might get a bit of a discount. Anything that is unsold when the shop closes gets taken to the kitchens where it will be turned into a number of 'value added' products. At the beginning of the following day the entire display is recreated from entirely fresh produce.

Something that I enjoy about visiting other Food Hubs is that, although many things are familiar, each one is also unique. For example, the Coventry Food Hub shares similar architecture to the Cambridge Food Hub, but at least half the products available in the shop are only available through this Hub. This is perfectly illustrated when I walk into the shop's 'preserves and pickles' aisle. Here I am confronted by shelves stacked with very familiar-looking jars; these are the very same reusable jars that are used in every 'Harmony Food Hub'. However, the contents of these jars are not the same as the jars in the 'preserves and pickles' aisle back in Cambridge. These jars have been filled by businesses who are operating in the incubator kitchens in the Coventry Food Hub, and the Cambridge ones are similarly filled by offerings from occupants of the Cambridge incubator kitchens. I purchase a jar of picked gherkins and some greengage jam. I know I will be able to return the jars to the Cambridge Food Hub for reuse, or indeed any other Harmony Food Hub.

By lunchtime I have made it as far as Stoke-on-Trent. I am feeling hungry and the car needs to be charged up. I pull into a roadside charging station. Roadside charging stations have cropped up all over Britain's road network in recent years. Some of the larger ones have over a hundred chargers, and they normally have facilities such as toilets and places to eat. The one just outside Stoke has a few of the chain outlets you might normally expect to find in such a place, such as a Greggs bakery and a Costa Coffee; however, I'm delighted to see that there is also a place called 'Curly Kale Café', which proudly announces that it is a member of Stoke's Local Food Ecosystem. Curly Kale Café is an independent business which sells freshly made sandwiches as well as pasties that are made by another local company. It is comfortably the most popular eatery on the site. I go for a roasted vegetable and hummus bap. The bread was baked that morning in a local bakery, the pepper, aubergine, courgette and onion were all grown locally, and the hummus made from

UK-grown chickpeas. I wash it down with an elderflower pressé that was made by yet another local business. All this food was delivered to Curly Kale by the Stoke Food Hub. The food isn't cheap, but I consider it excellent value for money given its high quality and provenance, as I recall how ten years previously it would have been unheard of to find such food in a roadside service station.

Forward-thinking dietary choices. UK-grown beans and pulses are a highly sustainable source of protein. Josiah Meldrum of Hodmedod Ltd. shows off some of the first ever chickpeas to be commercially grown in the UK.

As I continue my journey northwards I pass through some market towns and suburbs. I frequently spot independent food shops, not only on high streets but in suburban shopping precincts and villages as well, often proudly advertising local products of particular note: 'Local strawberries, £2 a punnet', 'Tomatoes; freshly picked this morning'. When driving past Skelmersdale I pass a 'Wigan Food Hub' van going in the opposite direction. I wave to the driver but he just looks at me blankly; probably thinks I'm a nutter.

I arrive at the Preston Food Hub late in the afternoon and the lady who greets me is keen to immediately whisk me away to visit a community food project that they are particularly proud of. I am taken to a district of local authority housing. A decade earlier this area was known as an area of deprivation, with above-average levels of child obesity and other diet-related diseases. The only food outlets in the local shopping precinct were three fast-food takeaways, and a convenience store which sold mainly crisps, sweets and a range of tinned foods. Fresh fruit and veg simply was not available. However, a few years ago a group of residents decided to set up a food-buying club; a group of families pooled their resources to buy food in bulk and save money. My host takes me to a community centre on the estate where the buying club is in the process of setting up as the residents who are members will come and collect their goods throughout the evening. It is a hive of activity. The buying club has proved immensely successful; more than 300 households are now members. The Preston Food Hub helped establish the buying club, and supplies them with locally produced vegetables along with all sorts of bulk dried foods like pasta, rice, flour, beans and pulses, which are sold at 'distributor rate'. The club pays the 'flexible-user' membership fee and as such are sent a quantity of fruit and veg each week that did not find a home elsewhere in Preston, but which is all very fresh and excellent quality. Not long after the club started, a group of members started a side-line enterprise preparing meals for other members of the community who were vulnerable or who were not proficient at preparing food. This venture eventually became a 'pay-as-you-feel' café which has now replaced one of the fast-food outlets in the shopping precinct. The convenience store also has a 'local produce' section now.

The members of the club work to a rota in which teams of a dozen people take it in turns to divide the food into parcels according to the needs of the members. This is what they are in the process of doing when I arrive there. There is a terrific atmosphere in the place; the people who are doing the work clearly enjoy the activity and you can sense the feeling of camaraderie. I stay for a few hours just watching people turn up to collect their food parcels and talking to a few of them about their experience. It is clear that many of them benefit enormously from their membership of the club; not only are they saving money on food and able to access healthy fresh produce, the project has also helped bring people together and the general health of the community is significantly improved. My day ends with a meal in the pay-as-you-feel café accompanied by my host from the Food Hub and some of the people who originally set up the buying club. It is a most enjoyable dining experience; great food and great company.

As I lie in bed in the evening I reflect upon the events of the day. My journey from Cambridge to Preston took me through a country that has embraced the concept of the Local Food Ecosystem. At every point along the trip I was never far from an outlet where I could have bought some terrific local food. And these outlets were always characterful independent businesses. A significant proportion of the food they sold was either grown locally, or made by another independent local food business, and sourced through their Local Food Ecosystem.

The UK in general is now a much more forward-thinking nation. Nearly all schools now serve school meals made from locally grown

Education is another important objective of the Food Hub project. In this picture a group of key stage-one pupils are on a field trip to Russell Smith Farms near Cambridge.

140

food. Many schools have an affiliation with their local Food Hub, not only for the supply of food, but also for educational purposes as classes visit the Food Hub for food-skills training and to learn about healthy and sustainable dietary choices. There are now fewer vehicles on the road, and mostly they are electric. In part this is because so much more food is being distributed locally, but it's also because people are travelling less, often working from or within walking distance of home, and also obtaining their food through home-delivery or a walk to their local shops rather than a drive to the supermarket. Planning regulations have been updated to ensure that the residents of any new major housing developments are able to access healthy, fresh food. As a result of this, many new developments and 'Healthy New Towns' now feature a Food Hub. The country has embraced alternative, 'circular' economic models. A thriving industry of sharing and reconditioning all kinds of consumer goods has emerged; tool and sporting goods 'libraries' have become a significant market sector, as has the industry for refurbishing furniture and electrical goods, and this has created lots of employment. Supermarkets and global food giants still exist, of course, and still account for the lion's share of the food market. However, the rise of the sustainable food/Local Food Ecosystem movement brought with it a shift in our culture and attitude towards food which the mainstream food industry responded to by improving the nutritional value of many products and working with farmers to adopt more sustainable production methods. Not long ago, a worldwide ban on intensive animal agriculture was imposed, and over 2 million acres of land in Brazil is now in a regeneration programme back to tropical rainforest. The Preston food-buying club is not at all a stand-alone project; many towns and cities have at least one such initiative. Instances of diet-related ill health have dropped by 30 per cent since 2015. It is estimated that the drive to combat obesity in the UK, in which the Food Hubs have played a big part, is saving the NHS over £1.5 billion every year.

How did the UK get to be this way? What happened over the last ten to fifteen years?

Well, here is my personal story of this period at least. At the time this book was published, my colleagues and I were struggling to establish the Local Food Ecosystem in Cambridge. There were a handful of 'early adopters' who had become the original members of the Local Food

Ecosystem, shops like Arjuna, Daily Bread, Organic Health, Radmore Farm Shop, Linton Farm Shop, Full Circle Shop, Meadows and Burwash Larder. We were still in the process of building the number of producers on our Open Food Network shopfront at the time, so it was difficult for us to justify the cost of membership, as indeed it was difficult for us to deliver on the promise of a route to market for the producers we were working with. Fortunately, these forward-thinking early members believed in the ethos of the Local Food Ecosystem and were prepared to stick with us and support us through the formative stages.

If you can think back to what things were like in the early 2020s you will recall that it was a turbulent time in politics. The country was just emerging from the coronavirus pandemic, and also had the headache of figuring out what to do after exiting from the European Union, not to mention the climate crisis. A great deal of emphasis was being put on creating resilience in the food system, using more locally grown food and working towards the UN's Sustainable Development Goals. There were high levels of unemployment, and many people who had been made redundant during coronavirus decided to turn their hand to starting small food businesses. These circumstances created the perfect context in which the value of the Local Food Ecosystem became obvious.

Around this same time, a local voluntary action group, Cambridge DEAG,[8] was working with Cambridge City Council to implement Doughnut Economics principles within the city. In fact, many cities in the UK were also making efforts to implement new economic models. The concept of the Local Food Ecosystem fitted in with many of the local council's objectives. This helped the Food Hub project gain traction and eventually led to a site for the Food Hub being identified.

A year or two later we were finally able to realise the vision of creating the Food Hub building. In fact, this book played its part in helping us achieve it, as first-edition copies were sold as part of a crowd-funding campaign. The opening of the Food Hub building was a momentous event.

---

8. Doughnut Economics Action Group: conducting a project to create a 'Doughnut Portrait' for the city of Cambridge, as described in the book *Doughnut Economics* by Kate Raworth.

The Cambridge Food Hub sparked interest up and down the country. I found myself being approached by people from other cities who were interested in creating a Local Food Ecosystem in their own area. Often they were people who had read this book. Many of the people who approached me were involved with local action groups such as their local Sustainable Food Places group, or Doughnut Economics action group, but sometimes they were simply enthusiastic individuals who wanted to do something positive. I was always willing to engage, and before long I found myself frequently travelling around the country to give talks at conferences or to attend meetings with councillors and action groups.

Once the Cambridge Local Food Ecosystem was well established, I felt the time had come to sell my shares in the business to an ownership trust which would hold those shares on behalf of the members of the Local Food Ecosystem and the employees of the company. I pledged to use the money raised through this sale to help establish Food Hubs in other areas. I started a new business called Harmony Food Hubs Ltd. The purpose of this company was very much about further developing the Local Food Ecosystem concept, and empowering others who wanted to operate a Food Hub in their own area. Sometimes this would happen through consultancy, sharing our own experience of establishing a Local Food Ecosystem with others who wanted to do the same, and sometimes undertaking the whole project ourselves, just as we had done in Cambridge. Before long, nearly every town and city in the UK had a Food Hub project of some description. Many of these were Harmony Food Hubs, but a great many more were completely independent projects, many of them an enterprise which started life as either an organic box scheme or a shopfront on the Open Food Network. Some followed the principles of the Local Food Ecosystem, others decided to do things their own way, but in many ways that is not at all important. What *is* important is that the nationwide network of Food Hubs helped the sustainable food movement to become a significant market sector and kept the UK on track for reaching its climate-change targets.

Benefits

Back to the present day. Back to a time before the completion of the Cambridge Food Hub, before the age of the Local Food Ecosystem, and to an age where mainstream food industry dominates and there is a bleak outlook for the planet. What is needed for us to transition from the present situation to the vision described previously?

The most important ingredient in this transition is, without doubt, *collective willpower*. The ideas contained within this book need to resonate both with citizens up and down the country who want a food system that is kind to the planet and who resolve to support that through their purchasing, and food practitioners who believe in the cause and are prepared to work in unity with other local enterprises to create a burgeoning alternative food system. The Local Food Ecosystem needs to be a movement.

The Local Food Ecosystem concept works better the more enterprises participate in it. The more members there are, the greater the number of connections that can happen between them. For it to be a movement, each individual practitioner needs to be able to interpret the principles their own way, appreciate their role in the functioning of the Ecosystem and, most importantly, clearly recognise the benefit of participation for themselves. To finish this book then, I am going to recap the benefits that each stakeholder and practitioner ought to be able to realise for themselves in a functioning Local Food Ecosystem.

1. Benefits to small-scale food producers and processing businesses

I am leading with this particular group of Local Food Ecosystem members for a couple of reasons. Firstly, while perhaps not the most significant group of members in terms of volume of food produced, they are certainly the most significant in terms of being indicators of a thriving Local Food Ecosystem. A thriving Local Food Ecosystem is characterised by a prevalence of smallholders and market gardeners who grow food especially for the local market, and of micro and artisanal food-processing businesses who use local produce as their raw materials and produce distinctive foods with passion. A thriving community of such enterprises has knock-on benefits for other members of the Local Food Ecosystem too: independent retailers have a supply of desirable and distinctive products to sell, growers have an additional market for their produce, and society in general benefits from the presence of enterprises which, as I described earlier in the book, embody a terrific quality of life for people.

Which brings me onto the second reason, which is that because these types of enterprises are so critical to the ethos of the Local Food Ecosystem, this also makes them the ones the system is intended to support the most. One of the main problems identified at the very start of the project was that it is very difficult to establish a small-scale food business. As such, much of the concept of the Food Hub is specifically about creating the conditions in which this type of enterprise can start up and prosper.

This group of members, therefore, stands to benefit a great deal from the existence of Food Hubs.

One important set of benefits which small-scale food businesses experience relates to access and route to the market. As a member of the Local Food Ecosystem, a small-scale food business has direct access to a large number of local food buyers. Many of these buyers will be the very outlets in which their products are best placed: independent food retail outlets, farm shops, delicatessens, cafés etc. The Local Food Ecosystem can also give small-scale food businesses access to markets that previously would not have been possible for them, including significant institutional food buyers, who could offer supply contracts that would really help these businesses to thrive. The Local Food Ecosystem overcomes the barrier to markets that is often faced by small-scale businesses, where buyers do not like to deal directly with lots of small-scale suppliers.

A significant barrier that small food businesses face when trying to access local markets relates to economies of scale. Consider an artisanal manufacturer of chutneys, who has eight different varieties of chutney in their range. A local farm shop would like to stock the products, but only has enough shelf space for three lines from the range. It orders twelve jars of each variety. One of the lines sells very well, the other two sell reasonably well, but not at the same rate. The situation is going to arise when the farm shop wants to restock the single product line which has sold out. In this scenario the manufacturer is either going to have to dispatch a small quantity of product to the outlet, the delivery cost of which significantly eats into the profit margin on the goods, or otherwise impose a Minimum Order Quantity, which is either going to make it very difficult for the retailer to manage their stock levels, or more likely put them off altogether. The Food Hub completely overcomes this problem. The Food Hub can deliver the one case of chutney to the farm shop along with the other local products the shop is having delivered. The Food Hub can hold stock on behalf of the sellers, so it can be responsive to the needs of the buyers, meaning products are never out of stock. When you are a small food brand the last thing you want is for customers to visit a shop with the intention of buying your product only to find it isn't there.

A particular way in which smallholders or market gardeners benefit from the Local Food Ecosystem is that they will find a destination of value for *everything* they produce, the entire crop. Farmers can grow crops knowing that there is going to be a buyer for all of it somewhere within the Local Food Ecosystem. No need to worry about unreliable buyers. No need to worry about produce being rejected due to aesthetic imperfections. No need to worry about shifting produce when there is a glut, or being penalised if a crop fails. Producers also benefit from improved access to their local market; having access to a range of local buyers means a more resilient market, and less downward pressure on price or reliance on a small number of buyers.

There are some additional benefits specifically experienced by small-scale food-manufacturing businesses. One is the opportunity to occupy the incubator kitchen units at the Food Hub. They have access to affordable space on flexible terms, and are therefore able to operate with significantly lower overheads compared to renting a small commercial unit. Businesses located in these units have unrivalled access to fresh, locally grown ingredients; they are literally stored in the same building. And their products can be dispatched via the Food Hub's distribution service.

Another is that they will be able to source fresh, locally grown ingredients directly from local producers at 'direct' prices. There could be particularly good opportunities for start-up businesses who are 'flexible food users'; not only can they access food at a lower total cost, their role in the functioning of the Local Food Ecosystem is important so they can expect preferential treatment by the Food Hub (e.g. they might have priority over space in the incubator kitchen units).

A small food business does not have to pay *anything* to experience the full spectrum of services laid on for their benefit by the Food Hub: introductions to buyers, free storage space for stock, ability to list and sell products on the trading platform, processing of orders and invoicing, and collection and delivery of stock. It really is a terrific deal. The way the Local Food Ecosystem benefits in return is by having a range of desirable, locally made products to distribute.

2. Benefits for large-scale food producers and processors

The benefit of the Food Hub for larger-scale farms and manufacturing enterprises is mainly simply an additional route to market. Sometimes the benefits do not have to be innovative and ground-breaking. At the end of the day, that is exactly what a production business wants: volume of sales and reliable markets.

Buyers in the Local Food Ecosystem are incentivised to trade first and foremost with other members of the Ecosystem, so that they get best value from their membership. This gives branded goods a competitive advantage, as buyers have a reason to choose the brand available through the Local Food Ecosystem over competitive brands of the same product type which are not.

There is opportunity for farms to develop local brand identity; rather than being a brandless commodity, the farm can take pride in putting their name and brand on their food, letting customers know that their food has been produced on a local farm and telling them more about the production methods adopted there. By creating a locally recognised brand, farms can add value to their produce and achieve a better return.

3. Benefits for buyers: retailers, cafés, restaurants, catering businesses

Enterprises which buy food through the Local Food Ecosystem experience three main advantages: access to local produce and products, an ethical supply chain and saving money.

The Local Food Ecosystem offers buyers unrivalled access to several local producers and food-manufacturing businesses. Often, these sellers will be exclusively marketing their goods on the trading platform, so the Food Hub will literally be the only place the buyers can obtain those particular products. The Local Food Ecosystem also makes it much more convenient for food buyers to have a relationship with several local producers; through the trading platform the buyers only have to interface with one system, place one order, have one delivery, have one 'compound' invoice to process.

Ethical and sustainable sourcing is something that consumers are increasingly aware of. Food sourced through the Local Food Ecosystem is not only locally and sustainably produced, it arrives at its destination with the smallest possible environmental footprint. Buyers who source food through the Local Food Ecosystem are also participating in a system that generates zero waste, and makes provision of food for low-income communities. Buyers are therefore able to demonstrate social and environmental responsibility through their buying habits.

For most enterprises, the most compelling reason for making a decision one way or another is the economic one. I am sure that almost every business would choose the more environmentally responsible option in nearly every case as long as there was little or no economic disadvantage in their doing so. The great advantage of the Local Food Ecosystem concept is that, provided buyers are savvy and ensure they get good value from their membership fees, they can not only behave ethically, but *save money* as well. As a member of the Local Food Ecosystem, the buyer can purchase goods from local sellers at 'direct' prices. That is, the same price they would pay if they turned up at the farm in their own vehicle and bought in bulk. If you factor in the costs that the buyer would incur were they to do this, the Local Food Ecosystem is actually the most cost-effective way of sourcing food. As long as buyers make good use of their membership, buying through the Local Food Ecosystem saves money compared to buying from the wholesale trade.

It is important to note that the Local Food Ecosystem is the most cost-effective way of buying food when comparing like-for-like products. If a shop or restaurant wanted to buy organic tomatoes from a local grower then the Local Food Ecosystem will hands down be the most cost-effective way of doing that; the price paid is the 'direct' farm-gate price, and the membership fee is less expensive than the cost of visiting the farm to collect the goods in person or the margin that would be added by a wholesaler. There is no cheaper way to get that produce. However, the Local Food Ecosystem may not necessarily be the cheapest way of buying non-like-for-like products; the organic tomatoes from the local farmer are still likely to be more expensive than non-organic tomatoes that have been imported from Morocco.

The triple bottom line

In the summer of 2017 the Food Hub was joined by Alice Guillaume, who did a summer internship with the project. It would be no exaggeration to say that Alice has been instrumental in the Cambridge Food Hub project, showing dedication to the cause and going on to become the project manager as the Food Hub began its operations. Alice is a Geography graduate from the University of Cambridge, and as such she often extolls the virtues of the following diagram:

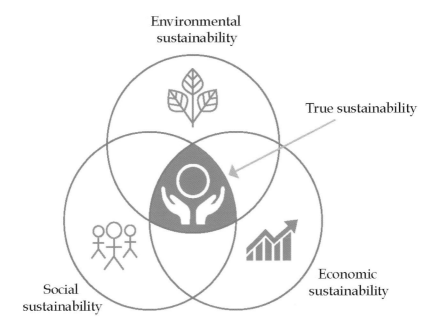

If the Local Food Ecosystem and the Food Hub are to be truly sustainable, it needs to be sustainable economically, socially and environmentally, and deliver benefit in all three areas. Let us consider how the Local Food Ecosystem performs in each of these spheres.

Economic benefits

1. Reduction in costs and emissions by doing things more efficiently

The social and environmental benefits brought about by the Local Food Ecosystem can overshadow the fact that it also has a significant *commercial* advantage over existing supply chains. Really, the greatest benefit of the Local Food Ecosystem is that it *just does everything more efficiently*, and things like reduced environmental impact and better access to healthy food for people on a low income are merely agreeable side effects.

The goal when designing the Local Food Ecosystem was to come up with a sustainable food supply chain *business*. So before we look at social and environmental benefits of the Local Food Ecosystem, we will first look at the economic case for it.

Really, the greatest benefit of the Local Food Ecosystem is that it just does everything more efficiently.

Let's start with the big one: food waste. Food waste has an enormous environmental cost attached to it, but it also has an enormous *financial* cost. Think of the money the farm that had to write off their field of lettuces in our earlier example had to invest in growing them: seeds, labour, water, soil fertility, machinery running costs. It would have been thousands of pounds. WRAP[9] estimates the total monetary value of food wasted in the UK each year to be £19 billion. Not all of this is the systemic food waste that the Local Food Ecosystem concept eliminates, but the economic grounds for adopting the Optimised Food–User Matching technique should be obvious all the same.

Supply chains add enormous costs to food. When food is subjected to a lengthy supply chain it is 'owned' by a number of enterprises along the chain, each of which wants to have their own slice of the pie (pardon the pun). Owning fresh produce brings with it the risk of its being unsold

---

9. The Waste and Resources Action Programme.

at the point of spoilage, and this risk needs to be reflected in the profit margin. In a lengthy supply chain the cumulative effect of a number of owners who have added their own percentage of profit not only adds to the total cost of food, but also puts downward price pressure on the producer, forcing them to lower production standards. In the Local Food Ecosystem the supply chain is as short as is possible. The Food Hub does not bear the risk of ownership, because it never owns the produce it is handling. Food buyers deal directly with food producers, so the unnecessary costs added by intermediaries are cut out, and both buyer and seller get a fair and competitive deal.

Transportation of food adds costs. Transportation costs are also exacerbated by lengthy supply chains. Shipping costs, fuel, drivers' wages, insurance, spoilage in transit – this all costs money. As was described in the section on micro-scale food miles in Chapter 4, the Local Food Ecosystem even represents a reduction in food miles over small food businesses taking their own goods directly to market.

And if you will excuse this rather stark way of looking at it, let's not overlook the fact that the social and environmental issues that the Local Food Ecosystem addresses also have massive financial costs attached to them. Diet-related ill health costs the NHS around £6 billion each year. The cost of environmental damage attributed to the food industry is incalculable. These are the externalised costs that the food industry does not currently take responsibility for.

2. Boosting the local economy

Trade between local businesses is a good thing. Healthy trade means good levels of employment, good social cohesion and good standard of living (think of the contrast between a run-down high street where every third shop is vacant, maybe a few betting shops and low-end fast-food joints, and a vibrant high street with no vacant premises, diverse shops, bustling cafés, hairdressers, and pretty much everything you might need within easy reach of your home). In a local economy money stays within the community, multiplying its effect many times over. Imagine for a moment that you are a chartered accountant, working from an office on your local high street. On your way home you buy some veg from a local greengrocer who sources produce from a local farm. The farmer employs two labourers. Those labourers enjoy a visit to the local pub at the end of the week. The publican employs two bar staff. They need to look neat and tidy for their job, so they regularly visit the local hairdresser. The hairdresser, pub landlord, farmer and greengrocer all need to get their accounts done, and come to you.

The Local Food Ecosystem facilitates local trade. Connectivity between local food businesses is improved no end, creating multiple opportunities to do business. This creates a fertile environment for new businesses to emerge, creating employment and fulfilling local needs.

Environmental benefits

Environmental sustainability always was the main motivation behind the idea of the Food Hub and the Local Food Ecosystem. The greatest benefits of the Local Food Ecosystem from an environmental perspective come from the elimination of waste, the reduction of emissions in the supply chain, and the encouragement of sustainable food-production methods and dietary choices.

1. Food waste

If you're reading this you probably don't need convincing that reducing the amount of food that is wasted is a good thing. Producing food uses a lot of land, water and energy. These are precious resources that we cannot afford to be frivolous with. Wasting food also wastes these resources.

By managing the food supply chain more effectively and balancing the needs of different types of food users, the Local Food Ecosystem is able to ensure that all food that enters the system finds a destination where it is valued.

Producing food uses a lot of land, water and energy. These are precious resources that we cannot afford to be frivolous with.

The type of food waste specifically eliminated in the Local Food Ecosystem is systemic food waste, food waste which happens along linear supply chains as an inevitable consequence of supplying food users with rigid requirements. The Local Food Ecosystem carefully balances the total volume of produce going out of the system with the total volume of produce coming into it, and it manages this by serving both food users who have rigid requirements, and those who can be flexible with regards to their inputs. When the system balances exactly, there is no waste. The more members of the Local Food Ecosystem there are, the more likely it is that balance can be achieved.

The scale at which systemic food waste is eliminated is proportionate to the size of the Local Food Ecosystem. No systemic waste occurs within the Local Food Ecosystem, but if that Ecosystem operates in a small city and only includes independent-sector enterprises then the extent of the food-waste impact is limited to the scale of that system. There is no reason why the Local Food Ecosystem principles cannot be applied to more sizeable supply chains, certainly on a regional scale, and possibly even national, to make the impact of this concept more widespread.

The Local Food Ecosystem can also help reduce other types of food waste by efficiently moving cyclable resources, such as donated surplus food from retailers and restaurants, between Ecosystem members.

2. Emissions in the supply chain

Food has to travel from its place of production to the place where it is eventually eaten. That involves energy and emissions. It is unavoidable. The Local Food Ecosystem performs this function in the way that causes the least emissions possible and uses the least energy.

The biggest way it does this is through coordinating the supply chain, and particularly the movement of food, in order to keep food miles as low as possible. This happens at the macro level, by creating direct trade links that enable food producers to access local markets and thereby maximise opportunities for food to be eaten in the area local to its production. It also happens at a micro level, by replacing multiple delivery routes made by a number of small-scale local food enterprises with one efficient delivery route, and transport emissions are reduced even further by both collecting *and* delivering goods simultaneously, and arranging 'circular' delivery routes which eliminate inefficient 'empty miles'.

The vehicles used for transporting goods throughout the Local Food Ecosystem are electric and charge from photovoltaic cells on the roof of the Food Hub building. Another big reduction in the environmental impact of the food supply chain comes from the reduction of energy used for refrigeration and the elimination of refrigerant gases.

3. Sustainable food production and dietary choices

These are two environmental benefits which do not come about as a direct consequence of the Local Food Ecosystem, but which are heavily influenced by it.

As a matter of principle, the Food Hub will not handle food which is the product of unsustainable farming practices. The whole concept of the Local Food Ecosystem is to create an environmentally sustainable food supply chain, so it stands to reason that the food handled within that system should itself be environmentally sustainable. The benchmark 'minimum' production standards that the Food Hub's policy will allow is LEAF.[10] Organic and Biodynamic are desirable production standards which will be encouraged by the Food Hub. It is hoped that the presence of a Food Hub in a Local Food Ecosystem area might encourage local food producers to adopt sustainable production techniques as well as to seek to market their produce locally.

The presence of a Food Hub within a community also encourages people to make better and more sustainable choices regarding the food they eat. The Local Food Ecosystem improves the prevalence of sustainably produced and locally grown food throughout the community. Better access to such foods makes it easier for people to choose them, not just in terms of the food they eat at home, but in their canteen at work, school meals, street food vendors, the buffet at a conference, the sandwiches in the petrol station. The Local Food Ecosystem improves the reach of sustainable food and the ability for people to choose it, even in situations where finding a healthy and sustainable option is currently difficult.

Most foods handled at the Food Hub are plant-based. This isn't necessarily because of a particular agenda of being vegan or vegetarian; it is mainly driven by the attempt to minimise energy used in the supply chain, of which eliminating refrigeration is an important aspect, so the Food Hub is 'mainly plant-based' by default.

---

10. Linking Environment and Farming.

Social benefits

1. Equitable distribution of food and improved access to healthy food for people on a low income

I am leading with this social benefit because, even though 'people on a low income' is only a section of society, it is an important one and it is good for society when *all* people are taken care of.

The fact that *hundreds of millions* of people in the world are hungry, and not just in developing countries but our own neighbourhoods, is the ultimate failure of the food industry. People who are experiencing poverty are segregated from the food system. Why? Because the food system is commercial and there is no opportunity to make money from people who have not got any. Feeding people who cannot afford food has therefore become the domain of charity.

This is completely unacceptable. The right to food is the most basic of human rights.

The significance of the Local Food Ecosystem's approach to making healthy food more accessible to people on a low income is that this group of food users are fully integrated into the system. All members of the Local Food Ecosystem are equally important to the functioning of the

The Local Food Ecosystem considers the food system as a whole. Members of the community who are on a low income are very much a part of this 'whole'. Here a van load of produce is being delivered to a local homeless shelter on Christmas Eve. In the future the Local Food Ecosystem can provide a much more systematic approach to the problem of food inequality.

Ecosystem. This means that the Food Hub provides a systemic solution to the problem of food poverty, with a sound commercial business model sustaining it.

2. Prevalence of healthy and sustainably produced food throughout the community

An abundance of good-quality, healthy food can only ever be a good thing for society. A well-fed and healthy populace is productive and happy, and does not overburden its health service.

The Local Food Ecosystem enables fresh, locally produced food to pervade all areas of the local community, meaning citizens are never far away from some healthy and sustainable food when they want it.

3. Meaningful jobs which enhance the workers' well-being

Earlier we examined the concept of creating business models which delivered value to their owners, customers, employees, suppliers, society and the environment in equal measure. Well, in true Orwellian style I am now going to suggest that one of these stakeholder groups is more equal than the others. And this stakeholder group is the employees.

If there were to be one group of stakeholders that should benefit from the activity of the company above all then they should be the people who are closest to it. People spend a third of their adult lives at work. This is a very significant amount of time. Life is precious. Time is precious. It is far too precious to waste it in an occupation which is boring or stressful or which fails to provide fulfilment. This is yet another of the great predicaments of the Capital and Growth way: people endure stressful and exhausting occupations in order to earn money, and then need to spend that money on holidays and leisure pursuits in order to recover from all the hard work.

Work should not be this way, and it certainly does not have to. An important aim of the Food Hub is to be able to offer positions of employment which enhance well-being: having a workforce of happy and motivated people who *love* their jobs.

This makes very logical sense from a business perspective. Employees are the lifeblood of any business. These are the people who are responsible for the day-to-day activities of the company. When the people are happy and functioning well, then the business itself is happy and functions well.

It should not be hard to achieve this.

Fair pay is a good start and paying the Real Living Wage[11] should be a given. The food industry is notorious for low-paid jobs. Margins are always tight when it comes to food, especially so when it comes to sustainable food. The Food Hub is never going to be able to provide its workers with affluence, but it will always provide *enough.*

However, level of remuneration actually has little bearing on whether or not the workers will love their occupation. What really matters is the actual *experience* of being at work. The work itself must be meaningful, stimulating and, to a certain extent at least, enjoyable. Being treated with respect, trusted and given responsibility. Enjoying the company of colleagues. Being safe. Having the correct equipment. Not experiencing stress. This is all basic and obvious stuff, yet many employers get this so wrong.

Another important thing, and a key part of the vision for the Food Hub, is the *place* of work. It must be a place that simply 'feels right' to exist within. Well lit, good acoustics, fresh air. They may be subtle details, but they are ever so important to the overall work experience. The Food Hub can provide workers with this and so much more.

Conclusion

The time is right. The world's economy has been turned on its head, as indeed have many aspects of our way of life. And this coincides with a moment in history when human activity is on the verge of reaching critical environmental 'tipping points' that will have catastrophic consequences. Now is the time to 'build back better', a sentiment I believe we can all get behind regardless of political persuasion.

In order to build back better it is important to have a vision of what 'better' looks like, and for us not to be afraid to try things which are radically different to the way things have been done up till now.

A vital ingredient of transformation is unity. Change will not happen unless many people are able to share a vision of what the 'new way' might be like, and are prepared to change attitudes and behaviours accordingly.

---

11. The Real Living Wage is calculated based on the actual cost of living. The Living Wage campaign is administered by the Living Wage Foundation.

In order to build back better it is important to have a vision of what 'better' looks like.

The Local Food Ecosystem is a vision for a better food system. If many people share this vision then the food system can change. But whether it is the Local Food Ecosystem that becomes the vision for the future of food, or an alternative vision that ends up uniting food practitioners and citizens, it is vital that we never again lose sight of what the purpose of the food industry should be: feeding people with healthy and sustainably produced food.

Epilogue

A few thoughts to leave you with.

The first is that this is not a vision for a 'niche' or 'alternative' business model. Companies and businesses that are built around principles of Harmony *are* the big businesses of the future. There are two important reasons why Harmony businesses will prevail while the incumbent Capital and Growth-principled businesses dwindle. The noble purpose of a business is always compromised when profit is the primary objective. In a Harmony business, profit can still be *an* objective, but its *primary* objective is the noble purpose. Because the Harmony business is able to deliver its noble purpose without compromise, it has a distinct *competitive advantage* over its rivals, and will ultimately supersede them.

The other reason why Harmony businesses will dominate the commercial landscape of the future comes down to the most basic of equations: the resources on which the incumbent economy is built are finite, therefore the lifespan of this economy is also finite. Our current economic model has, as its bedrock, a very arbitrary means of reflecting the true value of things. Climate change is going to very vigorously test the notion of value, and when this happens the companies whose business models are based on 'superficially valuable' commodities (e.g. gold) or 'stranded assets' (e.g. fossil fuels) are doomed. The new era of 'corporate giants' will be made up of companies who deliver true value to society, businesses that protect and regenerate the natural ecosystems which are so important for life on earth. Harmony businesses.

What an exciting time for those pioneers among us for whom being on the frontier during this time of transition presents a wonderful opportunity to establish the companies that will shape the world of tomorrow, and help define the 'new way' of being.

The second thought is on the subject of 'system change'. The fact of the matter is that I am not the Food Tsar of the world, and the industrialised food system will be with us for many years to come. Hopefully, we can influence and work with the mainstream food industry to help it move towards sustainability, but I think we are a long way off having a 'sustainable food system'. Earlier in the book I promised you that 'this is what system change *looks like*'. While I cannot promise to revolutionise the entire system, the Local Food Ecosystem is, at least, an ideal food system within its own microcosm, giving us a glimpse of what we mean by system change. The importance of demonstrating that it is indeed possible to do this really should not be underestimated.

The final thought to leave you with is that this is eminently possible. OK, perhaps reinventing the entire economic model is a little far-fetched, but a Harmony business can be founded today with just a little imagination and open-mindedness.

The Cambridge Food Hub has already begun trading. This was achieved, thanks to the belief and willpower of some extraordinary people, *with zero funding*. Much of the Local Food Ecosystem concept has now been proved in a commercial environment. If nothing else, the Cambridge Food Hub will be an interesting and *important* experiment in what Harmony in business and the economy might look like.

Acknowledgements

I feel it appropriate to begin the acknowledgements by thanking David Cadman. This book started out as an attempt to write an article for the Harmony Project website, in which I was experiencing difficulty explaining the Local Food Ecosystem concept within the word limit. It then became a paper which was shared with the 'Harmony in business and economy' group, and eventually evolved into the book you hold today. David, your encouragement and advice was highly appreciated throughout this process.

Indeed I would like to thank everyone else at the Harmony project, especially Bonnie Welch, Richard Dunne, Patrick Holden and Nick Campion, for giving the book their blessing and agreeing for it to be associated with this marvellous initiative.

I would especially like to thank Tristan Welch, Rosie Sykes, Heather Sturman, David Booth and Paul Robinson for so generously agreeing to contribute pieces of writing to the book, and to Kat Hiby for her terrific diagrams.

Tony Juniper is someone I have admired for many years, both for his outstanding work as an environmental campaigner, and also as co-author of the book that has inspired the concept of the Local Food Ecosystem. Tony, having a foreword written by you at the beginning of this book is a terrific honour for me and I would like you thank you enormously for that.

I would like to thank David Cadman, Alice Guillaume, Clare Morris, Madeleine Diment and Clair Heaviside for reading through earlier versions of the manuscript and making suggestions for edits. Thanks also to Ken Sewell of Janus publishing for so readily agreeing to publish the book in the first place, to Barbara Legg for her terrific work as the book's editor, to Tina Brand for typesetting the book, and to Shuk-Yee for designing the book's cover.

And finally I would like to show appreciation to all the people who have supported me not only through the writing of the book but the whole Food Hub project: the COFCO team, the Food Hub team, Brian, my friends and colleagues at Cambridge Sustainable Food and Cambridge DEAG, and of course, my Mum, Dad, sister Hilary, Cally, and my two lovely daughters Leona and Melody. I love you all.

All pictures by the author except the following:

Page 3, reproduced by kind permission of Steph French, and used with the permission of Clarence House

Page 20, reproduced by kind permission of Chris Roberts

Page 22, reproduced by kind permission of Chris Roberts

Page 88, reproduced by kind permission of Katherine Hiby

Pages 90 and 91, reproduced by kind permission of Katherine Hiby

Page 94, reproduced by kind permission of Zhiqing Li

Page 107, reproduced by kind permission of Alice Guillaume

Page 110, reproduced by kind permission of David Miller Architects (CGI Photon Studio)

Page 130, reproduced by kind permission of Charles Sturman

Pages 132–133, reproduced by kind permission of David Miller Architects (CGI Photon Studio)

Page 149, reproduced by kind permission of Katherine Hiby

About the author

Duncan's lifetime of experience with sustainable food began with his upbringing on an organic apple orchard in Suffolk.

In 1998 he founded the Cambridge Organic Food Company (COFCO), which was set up on a shoestring budget. Today, COFCO delivers organic veg boxes to more than a thousand local households every week, achieved while upholding strong ethical principles throughout. It has grown into a seven-figure-turnover enterprise.

A founding committee member of Cambridge Sustainable Food, the organisation responsible for Cambridge's inclusion in the 'Sustainable Food Places' network, this role led him to begin the Cambridge Food Hub project, which subsequently led to the development of the Local Food Ecosystem concept.

In 2015 he received the Living Wage Champion Award for the East of England, due, in part, to COFCO becoming the first food enterprise in Cambridge to achieve Real Living Wage accreditation.

He often gives talks and presentations about sustainable food, short supply chains and the Food Hub project at events, including the Oxford Real Farming Conference, the Harmony in Food and Farming Conference and at the European Commission.

Today, Duncan offers his expertise and experience to communities throughout the UK and beyond who wish to establish a Local Food Ecosystem in their own area.

For further information about this service please visit localfoodecosystem.org